D1466784

101
BEST PARTY QUIZ GAMES

By JACK SHAFER

with drawings by

DOUG ANDERSON

STERLING
PUBLISHING CO., Inc.
New York

OTHER BOOKS IN SERIES

101 Best Party Games for Adults
101 Best Stunts and Novelty Games
101 Best Games for Two
101 Best Card Games for Children
101 Best Magic Tricks
101 Funny Things to Make and Do
101 Best Action Games for Boys
101 Best Games for Girls
101 Best Games for Teen-Agers
101 Ideas for Clubs

The author has used as his authority on questions and answers the *Webster New International Dictionary, Columbia Encyclopedia, Encyclopaedia Britannica* and *Bartlett's Familiar Quotations.*

Table of Contents

How to Play
Party Quiz Games

Games of mental skill are always fun to play, especially when friends get together, and here's the chance to put your party or gathering into high-gear fun by pairing off individuals, or couples, in a competitive quiz, just as the big TV quiz programs do.

This book contains 101 interesting quizzes covering many different categories (see Contents). Each quiz is divided into four sections: 2-point questions which are relatively easy; 3-point questions which are more difficult; and 5-point questions which are pretty hard. The answers are in the back of the book.

With these questions you can make up your own quiz games, played under your own rules, but here are some suggestions of how "Party Quiz Games" can be played.

ONE PERSON can have lots of fun testing his own knowledge against each quiz and keeping score as he goes along through several quizzes. For example, the highest possible score on five full quizzes is 200 points (40 per quiz). A score of 110 or better is good; a score of 153 or better is excellent. It's exciting to see how well you can do!

TWO PEOPLE (OR TWO COUPLES) can play competitively—one team trying to answer the odd-numbered questions, the other team trying the even-numbered questions. If there is no one to act as Quizmaster and Scorekeeper, the contestants should write down their answers for the entire quiz *before* checking with the answer page; then go on with another quiz in the same way, and so forth.

The two team members must agree on the answer before it is given, just as is required on TV quiz shows in which couples compete. If they can't agree quickly, it's best to toss a coin.

However, it is usually more fun if a third person (or couple) acts as Quizmaster and Scorekeeper, checking each answer as it is given. This third person (or couple) can then play the winning contestant on another set of quizzes, with the losing contestant acting as the Quizmaster-Scorekeeper on the new round. It's usually better to play in teams, since some people become a bit embarrassed if in playing as individuals they can't answer some of the questions.

THREE PEOPLE (OR COUPLES) can play competitively at the same time and on the same quiz games by answering only questions 1, 2 and 3 in each set of questions, ignoring question 4. Again, unless there is a Quizmaster, the answers should be written down before they are checked with the answer page.

FOUR PEOPLE (OR COUPLES) can play, of course, by using all four questions in each set. Here again, couples that are paired off should agree on their answers.

LARGER GROUPS (such as Boy Scout dens) can play "Party Quiz Games" either by teaming up in groups of three or four or by playing different quizzes (four teams taking one quiz, another four a different quiz, etc., and then matching scores). However, there should always be a Quizmaster-Scorekeeper, preferably the Scoutmaster or a Senior Scout.

*   *   *

The quiz pages used can be selected in advance by consulting the table of contents, or they can be picked at random by some chance selection method (such as numbers picked from a hat). If only certain categories are desired (consult table of contents for titles), the group can decide in advance which numbers to place in the hat.

Ordinarily each quiz should be played straight down the page, starting with the 2-point questions, going on with the 3-pointers, then the difficult 5-pointers. However, if at least five quiz categories will be played in one complete game, a variation of the game might be tried by limiting each contestant to one turn per category—*but giving the contestant the right to pick the point value of the question he will try to answer* (the easy 2-pointer, the 3 or the difficult 5). Of course the winner (contestant or team) is determined by the highest score in the total number of quizzes played in the entire game.

Still a further variation is to *credit* a contestant with the proper number of points for a *correct* answer but *debit* him (subtract points) for an *incorrect* answer. In no case, however, is a contestant put below 0 in his total score as the game progresses. For instance, if a contestant gains a credit of 3 on the first round, but tries a 5-point question on the second round and *misses,* he goes back only to 0, *not* to minus 2. If you play the game this way, you should keep score as illustrated:

	Team 1		*Team 2*		*Team 3*	
	Game	*Running Total*	*Game*	*Running Total*	*Game*	*Running Total*
Game 1	3	3	2	2	5	5
Game 2	—2	1	3	5	—5	0
Game 3	3	4	2	7	5	5
Game 4	3	7	—3	4	3	8
Game 5						
Total						

It's within the discretion of the Quizmaster to decide whether or not a "borderline" answer is close enough to be accepted. Allowing partial credit is not advisable.

"Party Quiz Games" can be played twice or more by the same groups on different nights if the quiz category pages previously used are excluded from subsequent games. With 101 quizzes in the book, there is material for many games.

Literature

GENERAL LITERATURE—Part 1

Contestant 1: Margaret Mitchell wrote the book on which one of the greatest money-making movies of all time was based. The movie starred Clark Gable and Vivian Leigh. Name the book.

Con. 2: Name the famous British author who first described Russia as "the bear that walks like a man." One of his best remembered poems is "Gunga Din."

Con. 3: In what famous "legend" do we find Ichabod Crane?

Con. 4: In 1877, Anna Sewell wrote the autobiography of a horse, a book that profoundly influenced legislation on humane treatment of animals. Name the horse.

3-POINT QUESTIONS

Con. 1: Which tragic American poet lamented the loss of a love named Lenore?

Con. 2: In "A Study in Scarlet," the letters R-A-C-H-E were written in blood on the wall. Inspector Lestrade thought the murderer had been interrupted while trying to spell out the name Rachel. But what was the correct interpretation made by Sherlock Holmes, who understood German?

Con. 3: Tell whether or not the following people were purely fictional or actually lived: Beau Brummel, Lady Godiva, George Babbitt, Cyrano de Bergerac, Minnehaha, and Copernicus.

Con. 4: Name the great American poet, born in 1878 at Galesburg, Illinois, who has written epic poems about Abraham Lincoln.

5-POINT QUESTIONS

Con. 1: In Walter Scott's story, "Ivanhoe," a romantic character named Locksley appears. With which legendary robber character of English folklore is Locksley identified?

Con. 2: Jonathan Swift wrote a book which he intended as a great political satire. Instead, it has become one of the most famous in the juvenile book field. Name it.

Con. 3: The poet Dante was banished from the city of Florence and compelled to wander over Europe. He remained true through the years to the great love of his life. In 1292 he wrote a poem about her, entitling it "The New Life." Name the woman he so deeply loved.

Con. 4: From the John Milton epic, "Paradise Lost," name the Fallen Angel and his two children.

(Answers on page 124)

GENERAL LITERATURE—Part 2

2-POINT QUESTIONS

Contestant 1: In a novel Robert Louis Stevenson wrote in 1896, young David Balfour is sent to sea by a cruel uncle. Was that book "Kidnapped" or "Treasure Island"?

Con. 2: Getting nowhere at writing comedies for the stage, this French writer switched to science-fiction 100 years ago and wrote "20,000 Leagues under the Sea" and "From the Earth to the Moon." Who was he?

Con. 3: Name the King involved in Tennyson's "Idylls of the King."

Con. 4: A famous London detective of 19th century literature loved no woman but deeply admired a clever swindler named Irene Adler. Name that detective (whose best friend was a doctor).

3-POINT QUESTIONS

Con. 1: In 1516, Sir Thomas More wrote a book about an imaginary land where people lived in great peace and happiness under pure socialism. From the title, we added a word to our language to characterize any scheme which is too visionary and impractical. Name the book.

Con. 2: Name the book written by an English tinker during his twelve years in prison at Bedford for "unlawful" preaching. His name was John Bunyan.

Con. 3: In the 17th century, Cervantes wrote a book in which a poor country squire, crazed by the idea of chivalry, carried his enthusiasm for it to such a point that the excessive chivalry of the times was soon laughed out of favor. Name that great book.

Con. 4: Thanks to re-runs of old movies on TV, everyone knows that William Bendix starred in "The Hairy Ape." But who wrote the play on which the movie was based?

5-POINT QUESTIONS

Con. 1: In Sheridan's play, "The Rivals," one of the female characters constantly confuses words that are similar in sound but different in meaning (for instance, saying "Allegories are things that live on river banks"). Her name has become a symbol in our language for such mistakes. What is it?

Con. 2: An obscure pirate named Alexander Selkirk was marooned for four years on a South Pacific island. A great English author based a fictional book on Selkirk's experiences there. Name the book and the author.

Con. 3: Women have made a great contribution to the field of English literature. Name the women who wrote the following books: (a) "Adam Bede," (b) "Sense and Sensibility," (c) "Mrs. Miniver."

Con. 4: The longest sentence in literature runs for forty pages! It is spoken by a character named Molly Bloom. Name the novel and the author.

(Answers on page 124)

GENERAL LITERATURE—Part 3

2-POINT QUESTIONS

Contestant 1: In an attempt to show that good can triumph over evil, Dickens wrote a novel about a little orphan who runs away to London and resists the evil influence of Bill Sykes and Fagin. Name that orphan.

Con. 2: A Phrygian slave who lived in the sixth century B.C. told his short stories through animals who speak and behave like human beings. Name the author of those famous fables.

Con. 3: Name the Rodgers-and-Hammerstein-like team of England which collaborated on such excellent musicals as "The Pirates of Penzance" and "The Mikado."

Con. 4: What did the soothsayer warn Julius Caesar to beware of?

3-POINT QUESTIONS

Con. 1: Who woke up one night from a deep dream of peace, to find an angel in his tent?

Con. 2: Name the sailor in Tennyson's narrative poem who returned home 10 years after his shipwreck, to find that his wife had remarried, presuming him to be dead. He then nobly disappeared.

Con. 3: Name the author and famous short story in which two men living on an island off Charleston, S. C., find an old hidden treasure parchment that leads them to the treasure of Captain Kidd.

Con. 4: What is the name given that part of the 16th century in which British achievements in poetry and drama reached brilliant heights?

5-POINT QUESTIONS

Con. 1: A novel by Nathaniel Hawthorne relates a story of the persecution of Clifford Pyncheon by his cousin, Judge Pyncheon—but Clifford and his sister Hepzibah find peaceful years when the Judge dies. Hawthorne named the book after the home in which Clifford and Hepzibah lived. Give its title.

Con. 2: One of John Milton's great poems describes the pensive life. A companion poem describes the pleasures of a more joyful, meditative life. Name both poems.

Con. 3: In "The Merchant of Venice" three suitors for Portia's hand must choose from three caskets of gold, silver, and lead. One of the caskets contains her portrait. Which casket is it, and who chooses it?

Con. 4: Name the play by Eugene O'Neill which used the device of having the inner thoughts of the characters in the play break through the regular dialogue in the form of soliloquies.

(Answers on page 124)

GENERAL LITERATURE—Part 4

Contestant 1: What was the pen name of William Sydney Porter, who became famous for his short stories with a "twist" ending?

Con. 2: Which famous sailor in the world's great literature was surrounded by water but had not a drop to drink?

Con. 3: Sax Rohmer made a fortune out of what menacing Chinese character, usually addressed as "Doctor"?

Con. 4: Which Edgar Rice Burroughs series about a jungle hero got Johnny Weissmuller started in the movies?

3-POINT QUESTIONS

Con. 1: In what book do we find ruthless Wolf Larsen, who ran his ship with no concern for the welfare of his crew?

Con. 2: In what book does Sir Brian de Bois Guilbert die of his own passions?

Con. 3: What was the name of the fictional Minnesota town that was the home of Dr. Will Kennicott in Sinclair Lewis' novel, "Main Street"?

Con. 4: What was the name of the fictional New Hampshire town that was the locale for Thornton Wilder's play, "Our Town"?

5-POINT QUESTIONS

Con. 1: Name the Mississippi town that Thomas Sutpen came to in 1833, in William Faulkner's novel, "Absalom, Absalom."

Con. 2: Which country was the locale of each of the following novels: (a) "The Brave Bulls" by Tom Lea; (b) "The Wall" by John Hersey?

Con. 3: Which country was the locale of each of the following novels: (a) "The Bridge of San Luis Rey" by Thornton Wilder; (b) "A Fable" by William Faulkner?

Con. 4: In a great satire by Rabelais, name the following two famous characters: (a) The Last of the Giants, whose immortal achievement is his voyage to Utopia in quest of the "Oracle of the Holy Bottle"; and (b) his father.

(Answers on page 125)

AMERICAN AUTHORS

Contestant 1: What was the pen name of Samuel Langhorne Clemens?

Con. 2: Jack London wrote a book about a dog that escaped from civilization and led a wolf pack. Name that book.

Con. 3: Name Theodore Dreiser's great novel that involved murder on a lake.

Con. 4: Name the Sinclair Lewis novel depicting the dullness of the life of a small-town business man.

3-POINT QUESTIONS

Con. 1: Bret Harte was the author who wrote a story that created a romantic picture of life in California and became the granddaddy of all "westerns." Name that story.

Con. 2: Who created the Uncle Remus stories?

Con. 3: Name the author of "The Red Badge of Courage."

Con. 4: Name the book Upton Sinclair wrote exposing corruption and labor exploitation in the meat-packing industry.

5-POINT QUESTIONS

Con. 1: Name the author most closely identified with the "lost generation" of disillusioned intellectuals following World War I.

Con. 2: James T. Farrell wrote a trilogy (1932-1935) about the squalor of life among the poor Irish of Chicago. Name the trilogy.

Con. 3: Name the French painter whose famous painting inspired Edwin Markham's poem, "The Man With the Hoe."

Con. 4: Which man who later became President of the United States wrote a notable book in the 1890's entitled "The Winning of the West"?

(Answers on page 125)

SHAKESPEARE

2-POINT QUESTIONS

In what plays of Shakespeare do we find the following characters?

Contestant 1: Cassius, a conspirator, and Cinna, a poet.

Con. 2: Banquo, a general, and Malcolm, a prince.

Con. 3: Petruchio, a suitor, and Katharina, the girl he conquers.

Con. 4: Two family heads, Montague and Capulet.

3-POINT QUESTIONS

Name the plays of Shakespeare which open on the following scenes or locales:

Con. 1: Westminster Abbey.

Con. 2: The park of the King of Navarre.

Con. 3: The palace of Theseus.

Con. 4: A ship at sea.

5-POINT QUESTIONS

Name the woman involved in each of these cases:

Con. 1: Antony married this woman, who was Caesar's sister, but left her in favor of Cleopatra.

Con. 2: Richard II married this woman after arranging the murder of her husband.

Con. 3: Duke Orsino finally married this woman after discovering she was disguised as his page, Cesario.

Con. 4: Lucentio married this daughter of a wealthy merchant of Padua.

(Answers on page 125)

NAME THE POEM (OR PLAY)—Part 1

Contestant 1: "At length did cross an Albatross:
Through the fog it came;"

Con. 2: "Nail to the mast her holy flag,
Set every threadbare sail,"

Con. 3: "Theirs not to reason why,
Theirs but to do and die."

Con. 4: "Good night, good night! Parting is such sweet sorrow,
That I shall say goodnight till it be morrow."

3-POINT QUESTIONS

Con. 1: "Yet each man kills the thing he loves,
By each let this be heard,"

Con. 2: "And the stately ships go on,
To the haven under the hill;"

Con. 3: " 'What writest thou?' The vision raised its head,
And with a look made of all sweet accord
Answer'd, 'The names of those who love the Lord.' "

Con. 4: "How do I love thee? Let me count the ways—"

5-POINT QUESTIONS

Con. 1: "Tell me not, in mournful numbers,
Life is but an empty dream."

Con. 2: " 'You're wounded!' 'Nay,' the soldier's pride
Touched to the quick, he said:
'I'm killed, sire!' And his chief beside,
Smiling the boy fell dead."

Con. 3: "Last scene of all
That ends this strange, eventful history
Is second childishness, and mere oblivion,
Sans teeth, sans eyes, sans taste, sans everything!"

Con. 4: "Not a drum was heard, not a funeral note,
As his corpse to the rampart we hurried."

(Answers on page 126)

NAME THE POEM (OR PLAY)—Part 2

Contestant 1: "Once upon a midnight dreary, while
I pondered, weak and weary . . ."

Con. 2: " 'Shoot if you must, this old gray head,
But spare your country's flag,' she said."

Con. 3: "Though I've belted you an' flayed you,
By the livin' Gawd that made you . . ."

Con. 4: "Sunset and evening star
And one clear call for me . . ."

3-POINT QUESTIONS

Con. 1: "She walks in beauty like the night
Of cloudless climes and starry skies . . ."

Con. 2: "To a rag, a bone and a hank of hair,
(We called her the woman who did not care)"

Con. 3: "Come, fill the cup, and in the fires of spring
Your winter garments of Repentance fling . . ."

Con. 4: "We are the dead. Short days ago
We lived, felt dawn, saw sunset glow . . ."

5-POINT QUESTIONS

Con. 1: "The ship is anchor'd safe and sound, its
voyage closed and done
From fearful trip the victor ship
comes in with object won . . ."

Con. 2: "Hog Butcher for the World,
Tool Maker, Stacker of Wheat,
Player with Railroads and the Nation's
Freight Handler
Stormy, husky, brawling,
City of the Big Shoulders."

Con. 3: "The room was hushed; in silence rose
The King, and sought his gardens cool,
And walked apart, and murmured low,
'Be merciful to me, a fool!' "

Con. 4:   "The wind was a torrent of darkness
              among the gusty trees,
            The moon was a ghostly galleon
              tossed upon cloudy seas."

(Answers on page 126)

"BAD GUYS" (of Life and Literature) Part 1

2-POINT QUESTIONS

Contestant 1: In 1818 Mary Shelley, wife of the poet, wrote the forerunner of all "monster" stories with her tale of a monster created by a young medical student. Name the monster, played by Boris Karloff in the movies.

Con. 2: The F.B.I. shot down this Public Enemy #1 outside of a movie theatre. Name him.

Con. 3: Robert Louis Stevenson wrote a novel about a doctor with a split personality. Name the hideous person and personality whom the good doctor became under the influence of a drug.

Con. 4: This gangster, enriched by Prohibition days, was nicknamed Scarface. Who was he?

3-POINT QUESTIONS

Con. 1: Incited by his cruel treatment, the crew of a British ship staged the most famous mutiny of all time in 1789. They set the captain adrift in an open boat with 18 companions; then sailed the ship to Tahiti. Who was that captain?

Con. 2: This warrior in the army of Duncan, King of Scotland, aspired to be king himself and murdered Duncan at the urging of his wife. Who was he?

Con. 3: In Goethe's great drama, "Faust," by what name was the devil called?

Con. 4: This Russian monk had great evil influence on the church and court. Friends of the Czar murdered this monk to end his influence. Name him.

Con. 1: Sheriff Pat Garrett shot and killed this famous outlaw whose real-life name was William H. Bonney. By what nickname was he best known in fact and fiction stories of the early West?

Con. 2: Name the tyrannical German official whose assassination set off the wave of reprisal terror that produced the massacre of Lidice in World War II.

Con. 3: Edward Teach became famous as a ruthless pirate. By what nickname was he known?

Con. 4: Teach's sailing master was a cruel and reckless man whom Teach once shot in the knee "just for a lesson." When Robert Louis Stevenson wrote "Treasure Island," he immortalized that man's name by using it as that of a sailing master in the book. Who was he?

(Answers on page 126)

"BAD GUYS" (of Life and Literature) Part 2

2-POINT QUESTIONS

Contestant 1: This Roman emperor had his own mother executed, murdered his wife, killed a girl who wouldn't marry him, and then put many Christians to death after accusing them of burning Rome. What was his name?

Con. 2: This Sioux Indian chief headed the Indian forces which massacred General Custer's men. Name him.

Con. 3: This miserly character hated the Christmas spirit until Christmas ghosts reformed him. Who was he?

Con. 4: This King of the Huns was so cruel in warfare that he was called "The Scourge of God." However, when he ravaged Italy in 452 A.D., Pope Leo I persuaded him to spare Rome. Name him.

3-POINT QUESTIONS

Con. 1: Othello has become the symbol of all overly jealous

husbands. But who was the miscreant whose insinuations drove Othello to murder Desdemona?

Con. 2: This pirate had his headquarters on an island off Louisiana. He pillaged shipping in the Gulf of Mexico. However, for helping General Jackson at the Battle of New Orleans, he was pardoned by President Madison but soon went back to piracy! What was his name?

Con. 3: In Dickens' "Oliver Twist," what was the name of the unscrupulous old man who taught young boys to become thieves and pickpockets?

Con. 4: In the short story by Stephen Vincent Benet, against whom did Daniel Webster contend for the unfortunate Jabez Stone?

5-POINT QUESTIONS

Con. 1: In "Les Miserables," Jean Valjean was persecuted and hounded by an overzealous detective. Name him.

Con. 2: Name the general who, in Richard Connell's famous short story, "The Most Dangerous Game," lived on a Caribbean island (alone except for his huge servant, Ivan) and hunted helpless men whom he lured to the island as "game" for his hunting sport.

Con. 3: Name the Italian statesman who wrote "The Prince," a book based on the theory that maintenance of power justifies deceit and treachery in government.

Con. 4: As Spanish governor of the Netherlands in the 16th century, this tyrant executed over 18,000 people to maintain order. Later he conquered Portugal with the same brutality. He had the title of Duke. Name him.

(Answers on page 127)

WHO WROTE IT?

2-POINT QUESTIONS

Contestant 1: "Uncle Tom's Cabin."
Con. 2: "The Sun Also Rises."
Con. 3: "Little Men."
Con. 4: "A Tale of Two Cities."

3-POINT QUESTIONS

Con. 1: "A Connecticut Yankee in King Arthur's Court."
Con. 2: "Sonnets from the Portuguese."
Con. 3: "Moby Dick."
Con. 4: "Outline of History."

5-POINT QUESTIONS

Con. 1: "Confessions of an English Opium Eater."
Con. 2: "The Purloined Letter."
Con. 3: "The Life of Samuel Johnson."
Con. 4: "Two Years Before the Mast."

(Answers on page 127)

AUTHOR'S MOST FAMOUS WORK
Part 1

For what work (or works) were the following most famous?
Contestant 1: Homer.
Con. 2: Solomon.
Con. 3: Thomas Jefferson.
Con. 4: Benjamin Franklin.

3-POINT QUESTIONS

Con. 1: Samuel Pepys (pronounced Peeps).
Con. 2: Giovanni Boccaccio.
Con. 3: Geoffrey Chaucer.
Con. 4: Izaak Walton.

5-POINT QUESTIONS

Con. 1: Henry Fielding.
Con. 2: Dante Alighieri.
Con. 3: Thomas à Kempis.
Con. 4: Adam Smith.

(Answers on page 127)

AUTHOR'S MOST FAMOUS WORK
Part 2

For what work (or works) were the following most famous?

2-POINT QUESTIONS

Contestant 1: Jules Verne.
Con. 2: Herman Melville.
Con. 3: Harriet Beecher Stowe.
Con. 4: Victor Hugo.

3-POINT QUESTIONS

Con. 1: Edward Everett Hale.
Con. 2: Vincente Blasco Ibañez.
Con. 3: George Eliot.
Con. 4: Richard Henry Dana.

5-POINT QUESTIONS

Con. 1: Francis Parkman.
Con. 2: William M. Thackeray.
Con. 3: Charlotte Brontë.
Con. 4: Emily Brontë.

(Answers on page 127)

AUTHOR'S MOST FAMOUS WORK
Part 3

For what work (or works) were the following most famous?

2-POINT QUESTIONS

Contestant 1: Pearl Buck.
Con. 2: Erich Maria Remarque.
Con. 3: Theodore Dreiser.
Con. 4: Joyce Kilmer.

3-POINT QUESTIONS

Con. 1: Lloyd C. Douglas.
Con. 2: Stephen Crane.
Con. 3: Sinclair Lewis.
Con. 4: Hervey Allen.

5-POINT QUESTIONS

Con. 1: James Branch Cabell.
Con. 2: Edmond Rostand.
Con. 3: Sophocles.
Con. 4: Edmund Spenser.

(Answers on page 128)

AUTHOR'S MOST FAMOUS WORK
Part 4

2-POINT QUESTIONS

Contestant 1: A. Conan Doyle.
Con. 2: Robert Louis Stevenson.
Con. 3: Louisa May Alcott.
Con. 4: Lewis Carroll.

3-POINT QUESTIONS

Con. 1: Maurice Maeterlinck.
Con. 2: Edwin Markham.
Con. 3: Bret Harte.
Con. 4: Feodor Dostoevski.

5-POINT QUESTIONS

Con. 1: Henri Stendhal.
Con. 2: Thomas Hardy.
Con. 3: Gustave Flaubert.
Con. 4: Plato.

(Answers on page 128)

COUPLE THE COUPLES!—Part 1

Give the name of the other lover in each case:

2-POINT QUESTIONS

Contestant 1: Priscilla and ....
Con. 2: John Rolfe and ....
Con. 3: Rhett Butler and ....
Con. 4: Lord Nelson and ....

3-POINT QUESTIONS

Con. 1: Queen Victoria and ....
Con. 2: Robert Browning and ....
Con. 3: George Sand and ....
Con. 4: Abelard and ....

Con. 1: Rosamonde and ....

Con. 2: Pericles and ....

Con. 3: Mr. Rochester and ....

Con. 4: Polly Peachum (of "The Beggars Opera")
and ....

(Answers on page 128)

COUPLE THE COUPLES!—Part 2

Give the name of the other lover in each case:

2-POINT QUESTIONS

Contestant 1: Mark Antony and ....

Con. 2: Robin Hood and ....

Con. 3: Paris and ....

Con. 4: David and ....

3-POINT QUESTIONS

Con. 1: Guinevere and ....

Con. 2: Tristan and ....

Con. 3: Hero and ....

Con. 4: Jupiter and ....

5-POINT QUESTIONS

Con. 1: Evangeline and ....

Con. 2: Lochinvar and ....

Con. 3: Troilus and ....

Con. 4: Ralph Rackstraw (of "Pinafore") and ....

(Answers on page 129)

FAMOUS SAYINGS—Part 1

Who said the following quotations?

2-POINT QUESTIONS

Contestant 1: "Come up and see me sometime."

Con. 2: "I have found it impossible to carry the heavy burden of responsibility and to discharge my duties as King as I would wish to do, without the help and support of the woman I love."

Con. 3: "The world must be made safe for democracy!"

Con. 4: "Sixteen hours ago an American airplane dropped one bomb on Hiroshima." (said by an American President)

3-POINT QUESTIONS

Con. 1: "The only thing we have to fear is fear itself."

Con. 2: "I'll moida the bum!"

Con. 3: "The reports of my death are greatly exaggerated."

Con. 4: "For of all sad words of tongue or pen, the saddest are these: 'It might have been!' "

5-POINT QUESTIONS

Con. 1: "Don't sell America short!"

Con. 2: "Full many a flower is born to blush unseen, and waste its sweetness on the desert air."

Con. 3: "If there were no God, it would be necessary to invent Him."

Con. 4: "There is only one thing in the world worse than being talked about, and that is NOT being talked about."

(Answers on page 129)

FAMOUS SAYINGS—Part 2

Who said the following quotations?

2-POINT QUESTIONS

Contestant 1: "If the people lack bread, let them eat cake!"

Con. 2: "Give me liberty or give me death."

Con. 3: "I came, I saw, I conquered."

Con. 4: "I have nothing to offer but blood, toil, tears, and sweat."

3-POINT QUESTIONS

Con. 1: "I would rather be right than President."

Con. 2: "In time of peace, prepare for war."

Con. 3: "Yet each man kills the thing he loves."

Con. 4: "I leave this rule for others, when I'm dead—Be always sure you're right—then go ahead!"

5-POINT QUESTIONS

Con. 1: "Man is the only animal that blushes—or NEEDS TO!"

Con. 2: "Always leave them laughing when you say goodby."

Con. 3: "Don't fire 'til you see the whites of their eyes!"

Con. 4: "No man is an island, entire of itself."

(Answers on page 129)

FAMOUS SAYINGS—Part 3

Who said the following quotations?

2-POINT QUESTIONS

Contestant 1: "I believe this government cannot endure permanently, half slave and half free."

Con. 2: "I do not choose to run for President."

Con. 3: "Mad dogs and Englishmen go out in the midday sun."

Con. 4: "Oh, East is East and West is West, and never the twain shall meet."

3-POINT QUESTIONS

Con. 1: "You may fire when ready, Gridley."

Con. 2: "Damn the torpedoes! Full speed ahead!"

Con. 3: "There's a sucker born every minute."

Con. 4: "That's all there is; there isn't any more."

5-POINT QUESTIONS

Con. 1: "After us, the deluge!"

Con. 2: "The ability to make love frivolously is the chief characteristic which distinguishes human beings from the beasts."

Con. 3: "An expert is one who knows more and more about less and less."

Con. 4: "Accidents will occur in the best regulated families."

(Answers on page 129)

COMPLETE THE SAYINGS—Part 1

2-POINT QUESTIONS

Contestant 1: "Pigs ...."

Con. 2: "God helps them that ...."

Con. 3: "All hope abandon, ye ...."

Con. 4: "The proof of the pudding is ...."

3-POINT QUESTIONS

Con. 1: "You shall not press down upon the brow of labor this crown of thorn. You shall not crucify ...."

Con. 2: "Never in the field of human conflict was so much ...."

Con. 3: "The best laid schemes o' mice and men ...."

Con. 4: "Can we ever have too much of ....?"

5-POINT QUESTIONS

Con. 1: "I'd rather have an inch of dog than ...."

Con. 2: "There is a tide in the affairs of men,
Which, taken at the flood, ..."

Con. 3: "What is a cynic? A man who ...."

Con. 4: "You may tempt the upper classes,
With your villainous demi-tasses,
But ...."

(Answers on page 130)

COMPLETE THE SAYINGS—Part 2

2-POINT QUESTIONS

Contestant 1: "If a man bites a dog, ..."

Con. 2: "You're not the only pebble ...."

Con. 3: "A bore is a person who talks when you wish him ...."

Con. 4: " 'The time has come,' the walrus said, 'to ....' "

3-POINT QUESTIONS

Con. 1: "God's in his heaven: All's ...."

Con. 2: "Rose is a rose is a ...."

Con. 3: "These are times that ...."

Con. 4: "The wheel that squeaks the loudest is the one that ...."

5-POINT QUESTIONS

Con. 1: "Most women are not so young as ...."

Con. 2: "Let us cross the river and rest under the ...."

Con. 3: "Pessimism, when you get used to it, is just as agreeable ...."

Con. 4: "Woman would be more charming if one could fall into her arms without ...."

(Answers on page 130)

MYTHOLOGY—Part 1

Contestant 1: Who holds the world on his shoulders?

Con. 2: In Greek mythology, Aurora was the goddess of the morning and Boreas was the god of the north wind. What display of strange lights was named after them?

Con. 3: Name the half-horse, half-man creatures that lived in the mountains of Thessaly.

Con. 4: Aphrodite was the Greek goddess of what?

3-POINT QUESTIONS

Con. 1: By what stratagem did Hippomenes defeat Atalanta in a foot race?

Con. 2: The king-size cleanup job of all time was accomplished by Hercules when he diverted a river through stables that had never been cleaned. Name the stables he cleaned.

Con. 3: Who was the watchdog of Hades?

Con. 4: Who changed Odysseus' comrades into swine?

5-POINT QUESTIONS

Con. 1: The ancient Greeks had a myth about an animal, born from the blood of Medusa, that rode through the sky at will. Identify and name that animal.

Con. 2: The staff of Hermes, herald of the gods, has become the symbol of physicians. Name it.

Con. 3: Name the boatman who ferried the dead across the River Styx.

Con. 4: Name the father-and-son team who learned to fly on wings of feathers and wax invented by the father.

(Answers on page 130)

MYTHOLOGY—Part 2

Contestant 1: Who was the Roman god of love?

Con. 2: When he made his trip to Colchis, what was Jason in quest of?

Con. 3: Who performed twelve great labors?

Con. 4: On what mountain did the Greek gods live?

Con. 1: Name the man-eating, one-eyed shepherds who, according to Homer, dwelt in Sicily.

Con. 2: Who finally cut the Gordian knot with one stroke of his sword?

Con. 3: Which handsome youth fell in love with his own reflection in a pool and was changed into a flower that bears his name?

Con. 4: Name the Roman god whose two heads faced in opposite directions.

Con. 1: Why did Persephone have to spend 4 months of each year in Hades with Pluto?

Con. 2: Who was the bravest Trojan warrior in the Trojan War, and by whom was he finally slain?

Con. 3: Which Greek sea-god had the power to change his shape and form at will? (A word of that meaning in our language was derived from his name.)

Con. 4: For what animal did Daedalus build the labyrinth in Crete?

(Answers on page 131)

MYTHOLOGY—Part 3

Contestant 1: This hero of Homer's "Iliad" was dipped in the River Styx by his mother, at birth, to make his body invulnerable. Because she held him by his heel, that part of him remained vulnerable. Who was he?

Con. 2: Which beautiful Greek woman had "the face that launched a thousand ships"?

Con. 3: Who was the Greek god of wine?

Con. 4: Name the principal river of Hades.

3-POINT QUESTIONS

Con. 1: Who killed Achilles and by what means?

Con. 2: Give the name of the band of adventurers who sailed with Jason in his quest of the Golden Fleece.

Con. 3: In the Nibelungenlied, who won the treasure of the Nibelungs?

Con. 4: In Norse mythology, who was the god of thunder?

5-POINT QUESTIONS

Con. 1: Procrustes was a tyrant who fitted people to his bed by cutting off their limbs if they were too short or by stretching them to death if they were too long. Which Greek hero slew him?

Con. 2: The Trojan War, according to legend, was fought because a prince of Troy abducted the beautiful Helen, wife of the King of Sparta. Name (a) Helen's husband at the time and (b) the prince who abducted her.

Con. 3: If a man looked at Medusa, one of the three Gorgons, he was immediately turned into stone. Which Greek hero slew her, and by what means did he avoid looking directly at her?

Con. 4: Because he offended the gods, this son of Zeus was condemned to stand in water up to his chin. The water receded whenever he wished to drink, and when he was hungry luscious fruits overhead would swing beyond his grasp. Name him.

(Answers on page 131)

THE BIBLE—Part 1

Contestant 1: Name the Philistine giant whom David slew.

Con. 2: Who was the cousin and forerunner of Jesus who called on the people to prepare for the Messiah?

Con. 3: Name the most sacred city of Palestine.

Con. 4: Name the prophet who was swallowed by a great fish.

3-POINT QUESTIONS

Con. 1: Name the large fresh-water lake, in the upper region of Palestine, which is closely associated with the ministry of Jesus.

Con. 2: Name the "father" of the Hebrews.

Con. 3: What was the name of Paul before his conversion to Christianity?

Con. 4: In their conquest of Canaan, the Israelites took a large city by marching around it and blowing their trumpets. Name the city and tell what happened there.

5-POINT QUESTIONS

Con. 1: Name the three sons of Noah.

Con. 2: After serving his Uncle Laban for seven years in order to marry one of this uncle's daughters, Jacob was given a daughter he didn't want and married her. However, by serving another seven years, he won the wife he originally desired. Name each of these wives.

Con. 3: What official title did Pontius Pilate have?

Con. 4: How many years is Methuselah supposed to have lived?

(Answers on page 132)

THE BIBLE—Part 2

2-POINT QUESTIONS

Contestant 1: Which strong man of the Bible slew a thousand Philistines?

Con. 2: Which Jewish king dazzled the Queen of Sheba with his opulence and wisdom?

Con. 3: Who was the "Doubting Apostle"?

Con. 4: What twin cities were destroyed because of their wickedness?

3-POINT QUESTIONS

Con. 1: Who was the first Christian martyr?

Con. 2: Name the sister of Moses, who led the people in singing and dancing after the Red Sea was crossed.

Con. 3: Who was sold by his brothers to a band of Midianites, who then took him to Egypt where he rose to power and influence?

Con. 4: What prophet was taken up to heaven in a chariot of fire?

5-POINT QUESTIONS

Con. 1: Name the three officials before whom Jesus was tried.

Con. 2: Name the three successive kings of Israel before their kingdom became divided.

Con. 3: Jonah got himself into a lot of trouble by disobeying God's command to go to a certain designated city, sailing, instead, to a city in the opposite direction. Name those two cities.

Con. 4: Name the rich man who buried the body of Jesus in his own sepulcher.

(Answers on page 132)

THE BIBLE—Part 3

Contestant 1: On what tower being built to reach the heavens, was work stopped because of a confusion of languages?

Con. 2: Which King of Israel was once a shepherd boy?

Con. 3: Name the Philistine woman who betrayed Samson.

Con. 4: What city in Galilee was the home of Jesus in his childhood?

3-POINT QUESTIONS

Con. 1: Many a teen-age son rebels against the authority of his father, but what was the name of King David's son who raised an army in rebellion against his father?

Con. 2: Name the place of the final conflict between the forces of good and the forces of evil, as foretold in Revelations.

Con. 3: Name the woman for whom King David had such a passionate love that he arranged the death of her husband in battle in order to be able to marry her.

Con. 4: The second Book of the Old Testament gets its name from a Greek word meaning a way out. What is that name?

5-POINT QUESTIONS

Con. 1: Name the member of the early Church whose deceitfulness to the Church was denounced by Peter. Since then, his name has been applied to habitual liars.

Con. 2: For which Babylonian king did Daniel read the handwriting on the wall?

Con. 3: Name the Persian king who captured Babylon in 538 B.C. and allowed the Jews to return to Jerusalem.

Con. 4: How many plagues did Moses cause to be visited upon the Egyptians before the Pharaoh released the Israelites?

(Answers on page 132)

LEGENDS, TALES AND FABLES—Part 1

Contestant 1: This legendary hero of Switzerland was sentenced to shoot an apple from his son's head. Name him.

Con. 2: Name the cruel master who in "Uncle Tom's Cabin" had poor Uncle Tom flogged to death.

Con. 3: Name the spectral ship that haunts the southern seas near the Cape of Good Hope.

Con. 4: What will-o'-the-wisp pool of water did Ponce de Leon seek in Florida?

3-POINT QUESTIONS

Con. 1: In Francis Stockton's famous short story, a barbaric princess must show her doomed lover which of two doors to pick, in an arena. Tell what awaits him behind each door.

Con. 2: In which book is the Indian Uncas the hero?

Con. 3: Which legendary king of Phrygia asked the gods to make everything he touched turn to gold?

Con. 4: The end result of the appearance of the Angel Moroni to Joseph Smith was the founding of a new religious sect called The Latter Day Saints. What is another name for this sect?

5-POINT QUESTIONS

Con. 1: In American folklore, which famous Negro steel driver beat a steam drill down through the rock, then died with his 40-pound hammer in his hand?

Con. 2: Which 17th century English statesman and general told his troops to trust in God but keep their powder dry?

Con. 3: Name the common-sense squire who attended the overly chivalrous Don Quixote on his adventures.

Con. 4: In Chaucer's "Canterbury Tales," in honor of which saint was the party of pilgrims going to Canterbury?

(Answers on page 132)

LEGENDS, TALES AND FABLES—Part 2

2-point questions

✗ Contestant 1: Who was the merry chaplain of Robin Hood's band?

✗ Con. 2: Name the woman who rode nude through the streets of Coventry.

Con. 3: Which famous sailor hitched a ride out of the Valley of Diamonds on a fabulous bird called a roc?

✗ Con. 4: Who was Tom Sawyer's best pal?

3-point questions

Con. 1: Name the Three Musketeers in the novel of that name.

Con. 2: Name the imaginary monster in "Through the Looking Glass."

Con. 3: Name the fabulous Arabian bird that dies, burns itself to ashes, and then rises to new life from its own ashes.

Con. 4: Name the boy hero of "Treasure Island."

5-point questions

Con. 1: A Norse myth tells of two children who were kidnapped by the moon while drawing water. Under what names did they turn up in nursery rhymes?

Con. 2: Name the sculptor of Greek legend who fell in love with his own statue of Aphrodite, whereupon the goddess gave the statue life and he married her!

Con. 3: Attila the Hun was called the Scourge of God, but which conqueror was called the Nightmare of Europe?

Con. 4: Which nephew of King Arthur seized the kingdom in Arthur's absence? On his return, Arthur killed this nephew but was mortally wounded in the combat.

(Answers on page 133)

LEGENDS, TALES AND FABLES—Part 3

Contestant 1: The Egyptian priests told of a great island or continent in the Atlantic Ocean which sank beneath the sea thousands of years before their time. Can you name that legendary land?

Con. 2: Name the triangular stone at an old Irish castle that gives the gift of a glib tongue to all who kiss it.

Con. 3: This hero of the Arabian Nights spied on 40 thieves and learned that the words "Open Sesame" gave access to their treasure cave. Who was he?

Con. 4: Name the steep, high rock on the bank of the Rhine River where a beautiful siren (for whom the rock was named) lured river boatmen to their death.

3-POINT QUESTIONS

Con. 1: Name the runaway slave who befriended a lion in a cave by pulling a thorn from its paw. Captured later, he faced that same lion in the Roman arena and was spared.

Con. 2: Name the sword that young Arthur pulled from its position in a huge stone from which no one else could move it. Thereby he became the English king.

Con. 3: Name the Scottish king who, in his refuge on the Isle of Rathlin where the British drove him, learned the lesson of patience from a spider spinning its web. Seven years later, he was victorious at Bannockburn.

Con. 4: In Greek legend, the tyrant Dionysius of Syracuse condemned a man to death, but allowed him to go home and settle his affairs first, provided someone acted as his hostage. The man's best friend volunteered as hostage, and when the condemned man returned for execution, Dionysius was so impressed by their friendship that he granted a pardon. Name the two friends.

5-POINT QUESTIONS

Con. 1: An English drinking society had a theme song about a Greek poet who loved his wine. Francis Scott Key, who knew the melody, wrote the words of "The Star Spangled Banner" to that tune. Name the Greek poet for whom the music of the song was originally written.

Con. 2: Alexander the Great built a city to commemorate the name of his favorite horse. Name his horse.

Con. 3: Name the half-human dragon-monster that Beowulf slew.

Con. 4: Peter Pan taught Wendy and her brothers how to fly. Give the full names of Wendy's brothers.

(Answers on page 133)

NURSERY RHYMES—Part 1

2-POINT QUESTIONS

Contestant 1: When Polly put the kettle on, what was in it?

Con. 2: How old was the pease porridge in the pot?

Con. 3: What did Little Jack Horner pull out?

Con. 4: Where was Little Boy Blue?

3-POINT QUESTIONS

Con. 1: For what three people did the black sheep have his three bags of wool?

Con. 2: What did the Old Woman Who Lived in a Shoe give her children?

Con. 3: Monday's child is fair of face. What is Tuesday's child?

Con. 4: What did Simple Simon go fishing for?

5-POINT QUESTIONS

Con. 1: What was the only tune that Tom the Piper's Son could play?

Con. 2: When Bobby Shaftoe went to sea, what did he have on his knee?

Con. 3: What did Wee Willie Winkie cry as he ran through the town?

Con. 4: What did Old Mother Goose ride on when she wanted to wander?

(Answers on page 133)

NURSERY RHYMES—Part 2 X

2-POINT QUESTIONS

Contestant 1: What frightened Little Miss Muffet away?

Con. 2: What did Jack jump over?

Con. 3: What did Tom the Piper's son steal?

Con. 4: How did Georgie Porgie make the girls cry?

3-POINT QUESTIONS

Con. 1: Of what occupations were the three men in a tub?

Con. 2: What did mother cat tell her kittens they couldn't have, because they'd lost their mittens?

Con. 3: What did Wynken, Blynken and Nod sail off in?

Con. 4: Why would a person "Ride a cock horse to Banbury Cross"?

5-POINT QUESTIONS

Con. 1: When the owl and the pussycat went to sea, which objects did they take with them?

Con. 2: Name at least six of St. Nicholas' tiny reindeer.

Con. 3: In the nursery rhyme that begins "Monday's child is fair of face," etc., what is said of the child born on the Sabbath?

Con. 4: In the case of the Ladybird whose house was on fire, what was the name of the only one of her children who was still there?

(Answers on page 133)

ORIGIN OF WORDS

2-POINT QUESTIONS

Contestant 1: In Greek mythology, the Titans were a race of huge, godlike creatures in the earliest days of Creation. Which word did we get from their name?

Con. 2: The Greeks called the word-pictures which the Egyptians carved into stone "hieros" (for sacred) and "glyphe" (for carvings). What word did we get from this?

Con. 3: The Latin "scintilla" meant spark. Name our word of similar meaning.

Con. 4: The Greek word "bakterion" meant a small staff. When scientists first saw some germ cultures under magnification, some of the germs looked like a staff. What English word was derived from the Greek?

3-POINT QUESTIONS

Con. 1: In Greek mythology, one of the rivers of Hades was called the Lethe. The dead who drank of it forgot the past. In Greek, lethargos meant forgetting. Which related word do we have in English?

Con. 2: The Iliad tells of Stentor, a Greek herald in the Trojan War, who had the voice of fifty men. What corresponding adjective do we have now?

Con. 3: The Laconians of ancient Greece said very little, believing in action, not words. What word did their name give us?

Con. 4: A French soldier named Nicholas Chauvin carried his admiration for Napoleon to an absurd degree. Which word in our language today means excessive patriotism?

5-POINT QUESTIONS

Con. 1: Almost 900 years ago, a murderous sect in India practiced political executions at their own whim. They ate the drug, hashish, to whip up their courage, and were known as hashashin (hashish eaters). What word of closely related meaning did we get from the Indian word?

Con. 2: When the Arabs were a sea-going people, they had a title, "Amir-al-bahr," meaning commander of the sea. It has been changed a bit in getting to us, but which word in our language comes from this title?

Con. 3: Since Popes have no children of their own, the early Popes sometimes favored their nephews with important positions in the church. The Latin "nepotis" meant nephew. What related word do we still use?

Con. 4: When the Athenians wanted to banish a dangerous politician, they voted on it by writing his name on a ballot which they called an "ostrakon." If 5,000 ostrakons were cast against him, he was exiled. Name the word we got from that ancient Greek ballot.

(Answers on page 134)

Places

INTERESTING PLACES—Part 1

Contestant 1: Which continent is called the Dark Continent?

Con. 2: Which continent is really a large island?

Con. 3: On which continent did Western civilization and its culture arise?

Con. 4: Name the extensive mountain system in Europe which forms a 15,000-foot-high border between France and Switzerland.

3-POINT QUESTIONS

Con. 1: Do most of the earth's land masses lie north or south of the Equator?

Con. 2: The deepest trough in the earth's surface lies near the island of Mindanao in the Philippines (35,400 feet deep). Name the mountain range which constitutes the *highest* upward thrust in the earth's surface.

Con. 3: Is the North Pole a land area or an ocean area?

Con. 4: Name the sea which Columbus thoroughly explored on his last three visits to America.

5-POINT QUESTIONS

Con. 1: Name the wide, beautiful street along the waterfront in Shanghai.

Con. 2: Give the number of the famous U. S. Route which connects Chicago with Los Angeles.

Con. 3: Name the most famous of the old Roman highways, connecting Rome with Brindisi.

Con. 4: Name the island in the Pacific Ocean, 2000 miles off Chile, where hundreds of huge, partly finished, monolithic statues pose one of the great mysteries of archaeology.

(Answers on page 134)

INTERESTING PLACES—Part 2

2-point questions

Contestant 1: The Labrador Current carries many icebergs into or near the ocean trade-lanes. In which ocean does that current originate?

Con. 2: Name the island in the Tyrrhenian Sea, six miles off Italy, where Napoleon was first exiled.

Con. 3: Name the historically important body of water which lies between France and England.

Con. 4: Name the sea in Palestine which lies almost 1300 feet below sea level.

3-point questions

Con. 1: Name the river which, rising in the Black Forest of Germany and, flowing into the Black Sea, is the most important water trade route in Europe.

Con. 2: Name the largest city in Africa. It is one of the most important trade centers of the Mediterranean and is the site of many famous mosques.

Con. 3: Which two European countries are connected by the Brenner Pass?

Con. 4: Name the great mountain system of South America, which ranges from Venezuela to the Tierra del Fuego.

5-point questions

Con. 1: Name the Italian city where Michelangelo and Galileo are entombed.

Con. 2: In which Chinese city is there an area known as the Forbidden City, because during the reign of the Manchu emperors no people other than members of the imperial household could enter it without special permission?

Con. 3: Name the street in London where an infamous debtors' prison stood from the 12th to the 19th centuries.

Con. 4: Name the famous rocky hill or cone which rises above the harbor at Rio de Janeiro.

(Answers on page 134)

INTERESTING PLACES—Part 3

Contestant 1: What is the Scandinavian word for a narrow inlet of the sea, penetrating deeply inland between high cliffs?

Con. 2: Name the most sacred river of the Hindus.

Con. 3: Name the island west of Norway which was discovered and settled by the Viking Naddodd in 868 A.D.

Con. 4: Which is the longest river in Italy?

3-POINT QUESTIONS

Con. 1: Name the body of water which separates the mainland of South America from the Tierra del Fuego. It bears the name of the great explorer who first sailed through it.

Con. 2: What is the name commonly given the vast, treeless plains in the central part of Argentina?

Con. 3: One of the South American countries is called the Shoestring Republic because of its long, narrow length. Name it.

Con. 4: Name the Italian city where Columbus was born.

5-POINT QUESTIONS

Con. 1: Name the small, volcanic island in the South Pacific which Christian Fletcher and eight other mutineers from the "Bounty" colonized in 1790.

Con. 2: Name the carved-figure memorial to the heroes of the Confederacy, sculptured near Atlanta, Ga.

Con. 3: Name the street in England on which the Bank of England is situated.

Con. 4: On which African river is the 343-foot-high cataract known as Victoria Falls?

(Answers on page 134)

INTERESTING PLACES—Part 4

Contestant 1: Which large tract of land, purchased by the U. S. from Russia in 1867, was known as "Seward's Folly" (Secretary of State William Seward arranged the purchase) because it was thought to be just an area of "icebergs and polar bears"?

Con. 2: Which river in South America discharges so much rainwater into the Atlantic that the natural salt content of the ocean is reduced for almost 100 miles?

Con. 3: Which island off the African coast was Napoleon's final place of exile?

Con. 4: Name the world's most extensive desert.

Con. 1: Which Oriental city is known, because of its extensive waterways, as the Venice of Siam?

Con. 2: A French game of ball known as paille maille was once played on a street in London and gave the street its present-day name. What is that name?

Con. 3: Name the group of islands north of Scotland, famous for a breed of ponies which originated there.

Con. 4: In which state is the geographical center of the United States?

Con. 1: In which Canadian bay do the highest tides in the world occur?

Con. 2: Name all five of the Great Lakes.

Con. 3: What name is given the area of the North Atlantic which is famous for its floating seaweed? The Portuguese name for it means the Sea of Little Grapes.

Con. 4: Which park in London contains "Rotten Row"—a corruption of the French "route de roi" (way of the king)?

(Answers on page 135)

WHERE ARE YOU? (Name the State)
Part 1

2-POINT QUESTIONS

Contestant 1: Appleton, Madison and Oshkosh.
Con. 2: Alexandria, Lynchburg and Staunton.
Con. 3: Abilene, Texarkana and Amarillo.
Con. 4: Providence, Bristol and Newport.

3-POINT QUESTIONS

Con. 1: Cheyenne, Cody and Medicine Bow.
Con. 2: Blackwell, Guthrie and Okmulgee.
Con. 3: Billings, Great Falls and Missoula.
Con. 4: Sumter, Greenwood and Spartanburg.

5-POINT QUESTIONS

Con. 1: Aberdeen, Pullman and Yakima
Con. 2: Beaver, Brigham and Moroni.
Con. 3: Palestine, Cisco and Mission.
Con. 4: Hibbing, St. Cloud and Winona.

(Answers on page 135)

WHERE ARE YOU? (Name the State) Part 2

2-POINT QUESTIONS

Contestant 1: Covington, Memphis and Winchester.
Con. 2: Brookline, Lexington and Worcester.
Con. 3: Lake Charles, Arcadia and Baton Rouge.
Con. 4: Ann Arbor, Battle Creek and Kalamazoo.

3-POINT QUESTIONS

Con. 1: Lewiston, Biddeford and Kennebunk.
Con. 2: Buffalo, Rochester and Duluth.
Con. 3: Cape Girardeau, Carthage and Columbia.
Con. 4: Albemarle, Fayetteville and Goldsboro.

5-POINT QUESTIONS

Con. 1: Coffeeville, Cimarron and Emporia.
Con. 2: Broken Bow, North Platte and Pierce.
Con. 3: Auburn, Oneonta and Port Jervis.
Con. 4: Aliquippa, Chester and Derby.

(Answers on page 135)

WHERE ARE YOU? (Name the State) Part 3

2-POINT QUESTIONS

Contestant 1: Decatur, Mobile and Birmingham.
Con. 2: Flagstaff, Phoenix and Nogales.
Con. 3: Hot Springs, Ozark and Little Rock.
Con. 4: Redwood City, Bakersfield and Sacramento.

3-POINT QUESTIONS

Con. 1: San Mateo, Ventura and Long Beach.
Con. 2: Dade City, Okeechobee and Hialeah.
Con. 3: Aurora, Elgin and Decatur.
Con. 4: Ashland, Frankfort and Bowling Green.

Con. 1: Alamosa, Boulder and Greeley.
Con. 2: Americus, Brunswick and Buford.
Con. 3: Ashton, Blackfoot and Moscow.
Con. 4: New Albany, Brazil and Paoli.

(Answers on page 136)

WHERE ARE THESE RIVERS?—Part 1

2-POINT QUESTIONS

Contestant 1: Hwang Ho.
Con. 2: Yukon.
Con. 3: Danube.
Con. 4: Rio Grande.

3-POINT QUESTIONS

Con. 1: Brahmaputra.
Con. 2: Don.
Con. 3: Fraser.
Con. 4: Oder.

5-POINT QUESTIONS

Con. 1: Mekong.
Con. 2: Yenisei.
Con. 3: Murray.
Con. 4: Parnaiba.

(Answers on page 136)

WHERE ARE THESE RIVERS?—Part 2

2-POINT QUESTIONS

Contestant 1: Nile.
Con. 2: Amazon.
Con. 3: St. Lawrence.
Con. 4: Volga.

3-POINT QUESTIONS

Con. 1: Irrawaddy.
Con. 2: Tigris.
Con. 3: Mackenzie.
Con. 4: Ural.

5-POINT QUESTIONS

Con. 1: Ob.
Con. 2: Magdalena.
Con. 3: Euphrates.
Con. 4: Lena.

(Answers on page 136)

WHERE ARE THESE FAMOUS STRUCTURES?

2-POINT QUESTIONS

Contestant 1: The Parthenon.
Con. 2: The Great Sphinx.
Con. 3: The Colosseum.
Con. 4: Westminster Abbey.

3-POINT QUESTIONS

Con. 1: The Taj Mahal.
Con. 2: The Pantheon.
Con. 3: The Alhambra.
Con. 4: St. Mark's Cathedral.

5-POINT QUESTIONS

Con. 1: Mosque of St. Sophia.
Con. 2: The Duomo.
Con. 3: The Escorial.
Con. 4: Mosque of Omar.

(Answers on page 136)

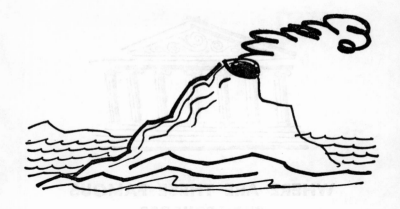

WHERE ARE THESE VOLCANOES?

Contestant 1: Mt. Vesuvius.
Con. 2: Fujiyama.
Con. 3: Mauna Loa.
Con. 4: Popocatepetl.

3-POINT QUESTIONS

Con. 1: Lassen Peak.
Con. 2: Paricutin.
Con. 3: Mt. Etna.
Con. 4: Kilimanjaro.

5-POINT QUESTIONS

Con. 1: Asosan.
Con. 2: Krakatoa.
Con. 3: Wrangell.
Con. 4: Colima.

(Answers on page 137)

STATE NICKNAMES—Part 1

2-POINT QUESTIONS

Contestant 1: The Peninsula State.
Con. 2: The "Show Me" State.
Con. 3: The "Cracker" State.
Con. 4: The Blue Grass State.

3-POINT QUESTIONS

Con. 1: The Cornhusker State.
Con. 2: The Cotton State.
Con. 3: The Pine Tree State.
Con. 4: The Green Mountain State.

5-POINT QUESTIONS

Con. 1: The Flickertail State.
Con. 2: The Sunset State.
Con. 3: The Beaver State.
Con. 4: The Bear State.

(Answers on page 137)

STATE NICKNAMES—Part 2

Contestant 1: The Hoosier State.
Con. 2: The Pelican State.
Con. 3: The Keystone State.
Con. 4: The Lone Star State.

3-POINT QUESTIONS

Con. 1: The Badger State.
Con. 2: The Nutmeg State.
Con. 3: The Sunflower State.
Con. 4: The Wolverine State.

5-POINT QUESTIONS

Con. 1: The Hawkeye State.
Con. 2: The Gopher State.
Con. 3: The Granite State.
Con. 4: The Boomer State.

(Answers on page 137)

INTERNATIONAL CURRENCY

In which country is each of the following used?

2-POINT QUESTIONS

Contestant 1: Rupee.
Con. 2: Lira.
Con. 3: Guilder.
Con. 4: Ruble.

3-POINT QUESTIONS

Con. 1: Tael.
Con. 2: Drachma.
Con. 3: Zloty.
Con. 4: Peseta.

5-POINT QUESTIONS

Con. 1: Pengo.
Con. 2: Escudo.
Con. 3: Dinar.
Con. 4: Markka.

(Answers on page 137)

SECTION III

History

1783

1499

1636

1864

AMERICAN HISTORY (Colonial)

2-POINT QUESTIONS

Contestant 1: Name two bodies of water in North America, discovered by and named for Henry Hudson.

Con. 2: On May 1, 1486, Columbus was introduced to a Queen of Spain who was very influential in getting needed help for his trip which resulted in the discovery of America. Name that queen and the king with whom she ruled.

Con. 3: Name Columbus' three ships when he discovered America.

Con. 4: What famous peninsula did Juan Ponce de Leon discover in 1513?

3-POINT QUESTIONS

Con. 1: Which Norse explorer evidently reached the North American coast around 1000 A.D.?

Con. 2: An explorer whose surname was Vespucci reached South America in 1499. What was his full name and his special relationship to the New World?

Con. 3: After Hernando Cortez defeated the Tabascan and Tlascola Indians, by which great Aztec Indian chief was he amicably received?

Con. 4: To obtain greater religious freedom, a group of separatists from the Church of England emigrated to Holland in 1608. Later (1620) they founded a colony in America. Name that group of people.

5-POINT QUESTIONS

Con. 1: The story of Pocahontas and Captain John Smith is well known, but can you name the maiden's father, the Indian chief with whom Pocahontas interceded?

Con. 2: Name the first English child born in the New World.

Con. 3: How many voyages in all did Columbus make to America?

Con. 4: Name the pastor of the Puritan Church at Salem who, upon being banished from that group in 1636, fled south and established a new settlement. Also give the present name of the city now on the original site of that settlement.

(Answers on page 137)

REVOLUTIONARY WAR—Part 1

2-POINT QUESTIONS

Contestant 1: Name the ship John Paul Jones commanded in his fight against the "Serapis."

Con. 2: Name the site of Washington's winter headquarters in 1777-1778, where his army suffered great hardships.

Con. 3: Name the mercenary German troops whom the British hired to help fight the war.

Con. 4: What was the name given the New England patriots who held themselves in constant readiness for action?

3-POINT QUESTIONS

Con. 1: In January 1776, a pamphlet titled "Common Sense" inflamed the Colonists with the idea of freedom and independence. Name its author.

Con. 2: The turning point of the war was an American victory on Oct. 13, 1777. Name it.

Con. 3: Which document, ratified by all 13 states by 1781, served as the first means of national government for the United States?

Con. 4: Name the treaty which formally ended the Revolutionary War in 1783.

5-POINT QUESTIONS

Con. 1: Which southern colony was the only one of the colonies which did not send representatives to the First Continental Congress?

Con. 2: Where did the official American flag, as adopted by the Continental Congress, *first* go into battle action in the war?

Con. 3: France entered the Revolutionary War by an open alliance with the American Colonies on Feb. 6, 1778. Two other

European nations also engaged in warfare against England during the war years, but without definite alliance with the Colonists. Name them.

Con. 4: A daring Kentucky officer lessened the peril of British-inspired Indian raids on the western settlements when he captured the British outposts at Kaskaskia, Cohokia, and Vincennes. Name him.

(Answers on page 138)

REVOLUTIONARY WAR—Part 2

2-POINT QUESTIONS

Contestant 1: In his speech before the Virginia House of Burgesses in 1775, what did Patrick Henry ask that he be given?

Con. 2: Where did the first definite military action of the Revolutionary War occur?

Con. 3: On May 10, 1775, Ethan Allen and Benedict Arnold captured a British fort on Lake Champlain. Name it.

Con. 4: From which European nation did the Colonies receive the greatest help in fighting the Revolutionary War?

3-POINT QUESTIONS

Con. 1: In 1765, the British Government imposed, for the first time, a direct tax on the Colonies, affecting legal documents of all types. It caused great opposition. Name that tax act.

Con. 2: Quartering British troops in the Colonies led to a lot of friction, and on March 5, 1770, British soldiers fired into an angry group of Colonists in a New England city, killing five of them. Give the historical name of that incident.

Con. 3: On December 16, 1773, a group of Colonists, disguised as Mohawk Indians, raided three British ships in a famous incident. Identify the incident.

Con. 4: From September 5 to October 26, 1774, 56 delegates from twelve Colonies met in Philadelphia to debate the emergency. They recommended that the people arm and form a militia. Name that body of delegates.

Con. 1: The legendary name of the battle was Bunker Hill. However, General Gage's forces took Bunker Hill quite easily. The real combat occurred at another hill, nearer Boston. Name it.

Con. 2: Name the British town where John Paul Jones brazenly landed on April 23, 1778 and spiked the guns of the fort there.

Con. 3: Name (a) the British general who tried to get Benedict Arnold to surrender West Point, and (b) the British agent who made contact with Arnold but was captured and executed.

Con. 4: The Battle of Lexington was provoked by a British attempt to surprise and capture two Colonial leaders who were agitating for armed resistance against England. Name those two men.

(Answers on page 138)

CIVIL WAR—Part 1

2-POINT QUESTIONS

Contestant 1: On April 12, 1861, shore batteries commanded by General Beauregard opened fire on a Union position, thereby setting off the Civil War. Name that Union position.

Con. 2: Which Virginia city did the Confederacy first pick as its capital?

Con. 3: When Virginia seceded, 50 counties of that state (tied in economically with the Ohio Valley) organized their own government. Later, those counties became a separate state. Name the new state.

Con. 4: Who commanded the Union forces on the "March through Georgia"?

3-POINT QUESTIONS

Con. 1: Where did the Monitor and the Merrimac fight their engagement?

Con. 2: The governor of a border state (Clarborne Jackson) tried to lead his state out of the Union in 1861, but he was unsuccessful when battles at Wilson's Creek and Pea Ridge established Union control. Name the state.

Con. 3: Who were the "Copperheads"?

Con. 4: The capture of New Orleans resulted when a Tennessee naval hero who had remained loyal to the Union got his gunboats past the forts on the Mississippi River. Name him.

5-POINT QUESTIONS

Con. 1: When the Confederate navy raised and rebuilt the U.S.S. "Merrimac," which name did they give it in renaming it?

Con. 2: At the dedication of the Gettysburg Battlefield on Nov. 19, 1863, Abraham Lincoln gave his memorable address. But who was the principal speaker scheduled that day?

Con. 3: Which Confederate general struck in sudden raids to within five miles of Washington, as late as July 11, 1864?

Con. 4: The Republican Party renominated Abraham Lincoln for the Presidency in 1864. Which Union general did the Democrats nominate as his opponent?

(Answers on page 138)

CIVIL WAR—Part 2

2-POINT QUESTIONS

Contestant 1: Which proclamation made by President Lincoln on January 1, 1863, affected all slaves in areas still in rebellion?

Con. 2: Which great Southern general was mortally wounded by his own troops, by mistake, at Chancellorsville?

Con. 3: To which general did Lincoln give supreme command of the Union forces on March 9, 1864?

Con. 4: At which courthouse did General Lee surrender to General Grant on April 9, 1865?

3-POINT QUESTIONS

Con. 1: On September 5, 1863, the United States notified England that if ironclad battleships under construction there were delivered to the South, "it meant war." England decided not to deliver them. Which two great Union victories of that year influenced England's decision?

Con. 2: Which Civil War general of the Union forces later wrote the famous novel "Ben Hur"?

Con. 3: Manassas Junction, Va., was the scene of two famous battles of the Civil War. Both were Union defeats. Name those battles.

Con. 4: On January 15, 1862, Lincoln appointed a new Secretary of War who remained in office for the rest of the war. Name him.

5-POINT QUESTIONS

Con. 1: Which Union general was called the "Rock of Chicamauga"?

Con. 2: Which French emperor offered to mediate the Civil War in February 1863 but was rebuffed by Congress?

Con. 3: With the United States locked in struggle, France openly intervened in Mexican affairs and forcibly set up an Austrian archduke as Emperor of Mexico. He was deposed and executed in 1866. Name him.

Con. 4: War between England and the United States was threatened when the U. S. Navy removed two Confederate commissioners from a British ship taking them to England. The incident is remembered historically by the name of that ship. Name it.

(Answers on page 139)

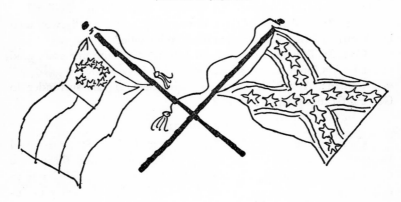

FIRST WORLD WAR

2-POINT QUESTIONS

Contestant 1: On May 17, 1915, a German submarine sank a British ocean liner off the coast of Ireland with the loss of 1,198 lives, including 124 Americans. Name that liner.

Con. 2: Name the commander of the American Expeditionary Force.

Con. 3: Which French general was given the job of coordinating the Allied armies on the Western Front in 1918?

Con. 4: Name the huge German cannon which lobbed shells into Paris.

3-POINT QUESTIONS

Con. 1: Who commanded the U. S. Naval forces abroad in World War I?

Con. 2: Who commanded the German spring offensive of 1918 that almost broke through to Amiens?

Con. 3: Name the first sizable action of American troops in World War I, when U. S. Marines stopped the German drive on Paris in June 1918.

Con. 4: Name the Austrian archduke whose assassination at Sarajevo on June 28, 1914 was a direct cause of the war.

5-POINT QUESTIONS

Con. 1: Name the first great naval battle of World War I and the two main naval forces involved.

Con. 2: To finance the war, the U. S. Government floated five huge bond issues. What popular names were given (a) the first four loans; (b) the fifth loan?

Con. 3: On July 24, 1918, the First American Army was formed as a fighting unit, independent of the French and British. Which famous salient of the front did that army take over in September 1918?

Con. 4: Name any five of the Allied nations. Then name any three of the Central Powers.

(Answers on page 139)

SECOND WORLD WAR—Part 1

2-POINT QUESTIONS

Contestant 1: Name the country which Germany invaded on September 1, 1939, thereby starting World War II.

Con. 2: Name the German general whose campaigns in North Africa earned him the soubriquet of the "Desert Fox."

Con. 3: On July 26, 1941, President Roosevelt nationalized the armed forces of the Philippines. Whom did he name as Commander-in-Chief of all U. S. forces in the Far East?

Con. 4: What common fate did these battleships suffer: Arizona, California, Utah, and Oklahoma?

3-POINT QUESTIONS

Con. 1: The destruction of ships played a big part in starting the Spanish-American War (the "Maine") and in getting the U. S. into World War I (the "Lusitania"). Name the U. S. river gunboat which Japanese planes sank on December 12, 1937.

Con. 2: How many airplanes a year did President Roosevelt call for in his budget message of January 3, 1940?

Con. 3: Name the great scientist, who on October 11, 1939, informed President Roosevelt of the possibility of developing an atomic bomb.

Con. 4: Name the French general who, after the fall of France in June, 1940, pledged continued French resistance against Germany.

5-POINT QUESTIONS

Con. 1: Name any three of the "Four Freedoms" enunciated by F.D.R. in his 1941 message to Congress.

Con. 2: Which large Danish island did the United States agree to defend, under an agreement with Denmark signed April 9, 1941?

Con. 3: On October 30, 1941, a German submarine sank a U. S. destroyer on convoy duty off Iceland. Name that destroyer.

Con. 4: On the same day the Japanese attacked Pearl Harbor (December 7, 1941), they also launched assaults on five other points in the Pacific area. Name any three of those places.

(Answers on page 139)

SECOND WORLD WAR—Part 2

Contestant 1: Name the man who led our first bombing raid on Tokyo in 1942.

Con. 2: Unchecked Italian aggression in Africa encouraged Hitler to expand territorially. Name the country in Africa that Mussolini's Italy invaded in 1935.

Con. 3: The world was shocked by a non-aggression pact between two world powers on August 23, 1939, which set the scene for World War II. Name those two powers.

Con. 4: Name the channel port from which England evacuated 300,000 men as France fell in May, 1940.

3-POINT QUESTIONS

Con. 1: What was the Alcan Highway?

Con. 2: Give the full name (in English) of Hitler's Nazi Party.

Con. 3: After Germany and Russia conquered Poland, there was a lull in the war that was finally broken by German invasion of two other countries, in April, 1940. Name them.

Con. 4: Identify the author and the men referred to in this quotation: "Never in the field of human conduct was so much owed by so many to so few."

5-POINT QUESTIONS

Con. 1: At Munich, what territory did England and France permit Hitler to annex?

Con. 2: An historic conference occurred in August, 1941, at sea off the coast of Newfoundland. The outcome was a document expressing the ideals and purposes of two great nations. Name the two men who met, and the popular name given that document.

Con. 3: Name the American ambassador to Japan who forewarned the State Department of a possible sneak attack, almost a year before Pearl Harbor.

Con. 4: Where did the British finally hold the line against the German drive on Alexandria and the Suez Canal in the summer of 1942?

(Answers on page 140)

SECOND WORLD WAR—Part 3

Contestant 1: After Manila fell to the Japanese on February 2, 1942, name the fortress to which General MacArthur retreated in Manila Bay.

Con. 2: Name either of the two Japanese cities on which atomic bombs were dropped in 1945.

Con. 3: In June, 1944, the Germans began bombing England with jet-propelled, pilotless aircraft—flying bombs. What were they called?

Con. 4: On the shores of which province in France did the Allied invasion (Operation Overlord) occur in June 1944?

3-POINT QUESTIONS

Con. 1: Name the military and naval commanders at Pearl Harbor, December 7, 1941.

Con. 2: Name either of the two British warships sunk by Japanese torpedo planes in the South China Sea, December 10, 1941.

Con. 3: Name either island of the Aleutian chain which Japan occupied in 1942.

Con. 4: Name the French admiral who became Chief of State in North Africa on December 1, 1943, but who was assassinated 23 days later.

5-POINT QUESTIONS

Con. 1: Name the first major naval defeat the Japanese suffered in World War II.

Con. 2: Name the final major naval engagement of the war.

Con. 3: On August 17, 1944, the U. S. 8th Air Force bombed an important ball-bearing works deep in Germany, crippling Hitler's war machine. Name either of the two German cities involved in the raid.

Con. 4: Name the great Russian city on the Volga River which the Germans entered on September 13, 1943.

(Answers on page 140)

KOREAN WAR

2-POINT QUESTIONS

Contestant 1: Name the important conference held in the Crimea in February 1945, at which Russia was allowed to have an occupation zone in Korea.

Con. 2: Which parallel divided North Korea from South Korea?

Con. 3: Name the President of the Republic of Korea, proclaimed at Seoul on August 15, 1948.

Con. 4: Who was named Commander of the U. N. Forces in Korea on July 8, 1950?

3-POINT QUESTIONS

Con. 1: Name the beachhead which the U. N. and South Korean forces tenaciously held in 1950.

Con. 2: Where did the U. N. forces land on the western shore of Korea, in MacArthur's leapfrog action of August 1950?

Con. 3: Name the valley where massive Chinese armies came into the Korean warfare on November 26, 1950.

Con. 4: Where was the main site of the armistice negotiations held during the summer of 1952?

5-POINT QUESTIONS

Con. 1: On October 14, 1950, President Truman and General MacArthur held an important meeting in the Pacific regarding the Korean warfare. Name the island where they met.

Con. 2: After MacArthur threatened China with naval and air attack, name the general whom Truman appointed to succeed him.

Con. 3: Name the Foreign Minister of the Chinese Communist Government who, on September 30, 1950, indicated that the Chinese would intervene in Korea.

Con. 4: Name the Communist capital of North Korea, which the U. N. forces occupied on October 20, 1950.

(Answers on page 140)

U. S. PRESIDENTS—Part 1

2-POINT QUESTIONS

Contestant 1: Who was the youngest man ever to assume the Presidency?

Con. 2: In his message to Congress in 1823, a U. S. President warned European nations against planning territorial expansion in the New World. Who was he?

Con. 3: Who was the only President elected unanimously by the Electoral College?

Con. 4: During whose administration was the amendment passed against a President serving more than two terms?

3-POINT QUESTIONS

Con. 1: Who was the first President inaugurated in the city of Washington?

Con. 2: Name the two signers of the Declaration of Independence who later became Presidents.

Con. 3: In whose administration did the Whisky Rebellion occur?

Con. 4: Which President had a "Kitchen Cabinet"?

5-POINT QUESTIONS

Con. 1: Name the two signers of the Constitution of the United States who later became Presidents.

Con. 2: Lincoln ran as a Republican in 1860 and as the candidate of the Union Party in 1864. Which was his political party when he ran for office in Illinois in the 1840's?

Con. 3: Name our only President who remained a bachelor.

Con. 4: Name the President who prevented war with England and Canada in the 1840's by resisting the cry "Fifty-four forty or fight!"

(Answers on page 141)

U. S. PRESIDENTS—Part 2

2-POINT QUESTIONS

Contestant 1: Weighing 310 pounds, who was the heaviest President we ever had?

Con. 2: Who was our tallest President?

Con. 3: Which President said he favored the policy of walking softly but carrying a big stick?

Con. 4: Which President was heartbroken when the United States failed to join the League of Nations?

3-POINT QUESTIONS

Con. 1: When Aaron Burr was Vice-President, who was President?

Con. 2: Whose picture is on our $20 bill?

Con. 3: Which President served the shortest time in office?

Con. 4: The landslide election of which President inspired the sarcastic remark, "As Maine goes, so goes Vermont"?

5-POINT QUESTIONS

Con. 1: Which President named Albert B. Fall as Secretary of the Interior and regretted it when the Teapot Dome scandal broke?

Con. 2: Which President was assassinated by Leon Czolgosz at Buffalo?

Con. 3: Who was our President during the Mexican War?

Con. 4: Name the President who ended the fearful days of Reconstruction for the defeated South by withdrawing the last of the occupying Federal troops in 1877.

(Answers on page 141)

FAMOUS MILITARY AND NAVAL NAMES

Identify the following:

(Answers on page 141)

2-POINT QUESTIONS

Contestant 1: The Argonne.
Con. 2: The Crusades.
Con. 3: Carthage.
Con. 4: Waterloo.

3-POINT QUESTIONS

Con. 1: Andersonville.
Con. 2: Black and Tans.
Con. 3: The Reign of Terror.
Con. 4: The Boxer Rebellion.

5-POINT QUESTIONS

Con. 1: Treaty of Brest-Litovsk.
Con. 2: Ladysmith.
Con. 3: Salamis.
Con. 4: Cannae.

THE WILD WEST

2-POINT QUESTIONS

Contestant 1: Name the victim in the gunplay involving each of these two pairs: (a) Buffalo Bill and Chief Yellow Hand; (b) Robert Ford and Jesse James.

Con. 2: One of the following characters was real. Which was fictional, Bat Masterson or The Cisco Kid?

Con. 3: Was prospecting for gold in a mountain stream called placer mining or stope mining?

Con. 4: Name the mill in California where the discovery of gold brought on the Gold Rush of '49.

3-POINT QUESTIONS

Con. 1: Did the last genuine gold rush in the United States happen in 1849, 1899, 1904 or 1944?

Con. 2: Which invention ended the days of the open cattle range?

Con. 3: Wild Bill Hickok and Bat Masterson were two famous lawmen. One died with his boots on in Deadwood Gulch; the other died in bed in New York City. Which of the two died in New York?

Con. 4: What famous event took place at Promontory, Utah, in 1869, involving two railroads?

5-POINT QUESTIONS

Con. 1: Name the two railroads which were linked together in 1869 to form the first transcontinental railroad.

Con. 2: The worst "bad man" of the old west was named after the religious leader John Wesley. What was his last name?

Con. 3: Name the last serious Indian uprising, which occurred in South Dakota in 1890.

Con. 4: Name the two-family gang wiped out by Wyatt Earp, Doc Holliday, and Earp's brothers in Tombstone, Arizona, at the O. K. Corral.

(Answers on page 142)

SECTION IV

Entertainment World

NAMES IN SPORTS

With which sport are the following identified?

2-POINT QUESTIONS

Contestant 1: Dick Kazmaier, Johnny Lujack, Jim Thorpe.
Con. 2: Paolino Uzcudun, Carmen Basilio, Tex Rickard.
Con. 3: Paavo Nurmi, Jesse Owens, Eddie Tolan.
Con. 4: Jim Bunning, Larry Doyle, Eddie Matthews.

3-POINT QUESTIONS

Con. 1: Carin Cone, Sybil Bauer, Clarence Crabbe.
Con. 2: Frank Sedgman, Maureen Connolly, Alice Marble.
Con. 3: Pete Rademacher, Tommy Jackson, Orlando Zuleta.
Con. 4: Bobby Cruickshank, Louise Suggs, Jerry Travers.

5-POINT QUESTIONS

Con. 1: Sid Abel, Al Rollins, Chuck Rayner.
Con. 2: Emil Zatopek, David Sime, Lon Spurrier.
Con. 3: Willie Mosconi, Welker Cochrane, Ray Kilgore.
Con. 4: Maurice Stokes, Bob Pettit, Harry Gallatin.

(Answers on page 142)

FAMOUS EVENTS IN BASEBALL

2-POINT QUESTIONS

Contestant 1: Who was the Giant first-baseman who was nick-named "Bonehead" because he forgot to touch second base on a hit which would have won the game?

Con. 2: Name the only pitcher who pitched three shutouts in a World Series.

Con. 3: Which pitcher holds the record for winning 19 straight games in a single season?

Con. 4: Name the only man who has pitched a no-hit game in the World Series.

3-POINT QUESTIONS

Con. 1: The longest major league game went 26 innings to a 1—1 tie. Name the two teams.

Con. 2: Name the only pitcher who ever pitched two no-hit games in a row.

Con. 3: Name the pitcher who won 33 games, including 16 shutouts, in one season.

Con. 4: Name the player who hit the most (23) grand-slam home runs.

5-POINT QUESTIONS

Con. 1: In modern major league history, seven hitters have hit .400 or better in a full season. Name any five of them.

Con. 2: Joe DiMaggio holds the record for hitting safely in consecutive games. How long was his streak?

Con. 3: The Giants hold the record for winning the greatest number of games in a row. How many did they run up?

Con. 4: Which pitcher has the best won-lost record in World Series games?

(Answers on page 143)

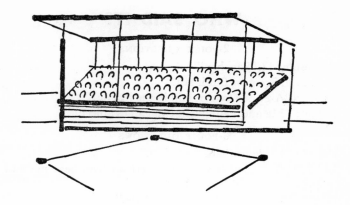

BASEBALL NICKNAMES

Give the real names of each of the following:

2-POINT QUESTIONS

Contestant 1: Georgia Peach.
Con. 2: The Scooter.
Con. 3: Fordham Flash.
Con. 4: Big Poison.

3-POINT QUESTIONS

Con. 1: The Big Train.
Con. 2: Preacher.
Con. 3: Schoolboy.
Con. 4: Memphis Bill.

5-POINT QUESTIONS

Con. 1: The Cat.
Con. 2: The Flying Dutchman.
Con. 3: Pistol Pete.
Con. 4: Black Mike.

(Answers on page 143)

WHO SAID IT?

Contestant 1: "Say, hey!"

Con. 2: "Nice guys finish last."

Con. 3: "Are the Dodgers still in the league?"

Con. 4: "Me and Paul'll win two games apiece!"

3-POINT QUESTIONS

Con. 1: "Hit 'em where they ain't."

Con. 2: "I'm glad it was an American who beat me and the championship stays in this country."

Con. 3: "He can run but he can't hide."

Con. 4: "The Giants is dead!"

5-POINT QUESTIONS

Con. 1: "Say it ain't so, Joe."

Con. 2: "We wuz robbed!"

Con. 3: "The bigger they come, the harder they fall."

Con. 4: "Avoid fried meats, which angry up the blood—and don't look back; something might be gaining on you."

(Answers on page 143)

POPULAR MUSIC—Part 1

2-POINT QUESTIONS

Contestant 1: In "South Pacific," the sailors agreed in song that there is simply nothing in the world like a certain object. Name it.

Con. 2: What was it that Annie Oakley found quite useless in trying to get a man?

Con. 3: A song in "Finian's Rainbow" asks how things are in a town with an odd name. Name that town.

Con. 4: In "Oklahoma," what was it that Curley and Laura were afraid people would say?

3-POINT QUESTIONS

Con. 1: Which famous western railroad became the song title of a hit tune written by Johnny Mercer?

Con. 2: Give the English translation of "Besame Mucho."

Con. 3: The name of which American city became the title of a popular dance step in the 1920's?

Con. 4: In "Call Me Mister," which geographical area did songwriter Harold Arlen call upon to "take it away"?

5-POINT QUESTIONS

Con. 1: Which concerto by Rachmaninoff supplied the inspiration for the popular song "Full Moon and Empty Arms"?

Con. 2: Upon which play by Ferenc Molnar did Rodgers and Hammerstein base their musical, "Carousel"?

Con. 3: Buddy Kaye and Ted Mossman wrote the hit tune of 1945 in "Till the End of Time." Upon which classical composition of Chopin's was it based?

Con. 4: The ever popular "I'm Always Chasing Rainbows" was based on which other Chopin composition?

(Answers on page 144)

POPULAR MUSIC—Part 2

2-POINT QUESTIONS

Contestant 1: Omar Khayyam said he wanted three things: "a loaf of bread, a jug of wine, and thou." In writing their hit song of 1934, Howard Dietz and Arthur Schwartz also waxed poetic about three things: "You and the Night and the ...." What was the third thing they specified?

Con. 2: Which business did Ethel Merman find incomparable in "Annie, Get Your Gun"?

Con. 3: In 1917, George M. Cohan wrote the hit song of World War I, even though when singing it in vaudeville he forgot the words! Name that song.

Con. 4: Name the hit song of Walt Disney's "Pinocchio."

3-POINT QUESTIONS

Con. 1: What kind of a "sky" did Hoagy Carmichael write about?

Con. 2: Lew Leslie's "Blackbirds of 1939" introduced a beautiful girl singer who in 1957 appeared in another Broadway musical hit. Name her.

Con. 3: Name the newspaper columnist who wrote "Goldmine in the Sky."

Con. 4: In 1928, Al Jolson and Warner Brothers made motion-picture history with the first talking-movie musical. Al's hit song in it was "Sonny Boy." Name the picture.

5-POINT QUESTIONS

Con. 1: In World War II, the German troops in North Africa sang a sentimental barracks tune which the Allied troops soon took over, also. It was the outstanding song of the war front (not the home front). Name it.

Con. 2: Which popular American composer once served with the French Foreign Legion?

Con. 3: Larry Clinton's popular song hit, "My Reverie," was directly borrowed from a classical composition. Name the original composer.

Con. 4: "St. Louis Blues," probably the greatest blues song of all time, was published in 1914. Name its composer.

(Answers on page 144)

CLASSICAL MUSIC

2-POINT QUESTIONS

Contestant 1: Name the composer of the operas "Tannhauser" and "Lohengrin."

Con. 2: Name the composer of ten successful operas, including "Rigoletto" and "Il Trovatore." He also wrote "Aida" to celebrate the opening of the Suez Canal in 1871.

Con. 3: Name the most popular Norwegian composer, whose compositions for piano and violin are notable.

Con. 4: Name America's first great composer of native music, whose songs include "Camptown Races" and "My Old Kentucky Home."

3-POINT QUESTIONS

Con. 1: This French composer, who abhorred sentimentality in music, wrote such instrumental formalizations as his "Bolero." He went insane and died in Paris in 1937.

Con. 2: This pupil of Haydn wrote only one opera, "Fidelio." He dedicated his beautiful "Eroica" symphony to Napoleon. Later in life he became totally deaf.

Con. 3: Name the Polish musician who emigrated to Paris and wrote only for the piano. He was the first great composer to put the folk music of a nation into classical expression. Tin Pan Alley has borrowed heavily from his compositions.

Con. 4: This great Russian composer and concert pianist wrote piano solos among the best of all time and all nations.

5-POINT QUESTIONS

Con. 1: Name the great French composer who wrote in all music forms, including the symphonic poem, "Danse Macabre" and the opera, "Samson et Delilah."

Con. 2: The Renaissance, with its emphasis on the rights of

the individual, had a great influence on music and ultimately on the creation of which form of music featuring dramatic recitative expression?

Con. 3: Which great German composer of the 17th–18th centuries spent most of his life in England? Turning from opera to the oratorio, he was instrumental in developing the English art of choral singing. Among other oratorios, he wrote "The Messiah."

Con. 4: Name the Austrian musician who first developed the string quartet and the sonata to the music forms by which they are known today.

(Answers on page 144)

OPERAS

Identify the opera in which the following actions take place:

2-POINT QUESTIONS

Contestant 1: Pinkerton, an officer of the U. S. Navy, marries a Japanese girl, Cio-Cio-San, who later commits hari-kari.

Con. 2: A man is about to kill himself when Mephistopheles appears and offers him youth in exchange for his soul.

Con. 3: A little boy and girl get lost in the woods while picking berries and are captured by the witch of the forest who is later trapped in the oven she planned to bake them in.

Con. 4: A beautiful Spanish girl is arrested for brawling in the cigarette factory where she works. The sergeant guarding her permits her to escape.

3-POINT QUESTIONS

Con. 1: A poet, a painter, a philosopher, and a musician are starving in a Paris attic. The poet meets and falls in love with Mimi, a little seamstress.

Con. 2: The woman-owner of a saloon in the California of 1849, falls in love with an outlaw and plays poker with the sheriff for his life.

Con. 3: A minstrel deserts his native village to live with the

goddess Venus. At the end he dies repentant (for his sensual love) and is saved.

Con. 4: The story of this opera revolves around a girl who has been stolen by a band of gypsies but remembers her childhood in a land where orange trees grew. When her real identity is discovered, it restores her father's sanity and straightens out the circumstances of her own love.

5-POINT QUESTIONS

Con. 1: The daughter of a fanatic Hindu priest falls in love with Gerald, an army officer, and meets him on forbidden grounds. Eventually the girl drinks poison and dies in his arms.

Con. 2: On her marriage night Lucy, whose brother has tricked her into marrying Arthur, whom she doesn't love, murders her husband and dies in the famous "Mad Scene."

Con. 3: A hunchback court jester mocks several of the noblemen of the court because the Prince has seduced their wives. Later, the jester plans the Prince's murder but the plot goes wrong and the jester's daughter is murdered instead.

Con. 4: A young monk fasting in the desert has a vision of a beautiful courtesan whom he decides to save from sin. He wins her to confession, and leaves her in a convent but later realizes he has fallen in love with her.

(Answers on page 144)

THEME SONGS

Which well-known people have used the following as theme songs?

2-POINT QUESTIONS

Contestant 1: "My Heart Belongs to Daddy."
Con. 2: "Love In Bloom."
Con. 3: "Some Enchanted Evening."
Con. 4: "I'm a Yankee-Doodle Dandy."

3-POINT QUESTIONS

Con. 1: "Heartbreak Hotel."
Con. 2: "April Showers."
Con. 3: "That's My Desire."
Con. 4: "Thanks for the Memory."

5-POINT QUESTIONS

Con. 1: "Rhapsody in Blue."
Con. 2: "Bali Hai."
Con. 3: "Rum and Coca Cola."
Con. 4: "Harvest Moon."

(Answers on page 145)

SHOW BUSINESS

2-POINT QUESTIONS

Contestant 1: Their "Hellzapoppin" was a hit of the World's Fair in 1939. Name this comedy team.

Con. 2: Strangely, Al Jolson and George M. Cohan never played the top vaudeville theatre of them all. What was that famous Broadway vaudeville house?

Con. 3: "The King and I" brought which bald-headed actor into leading man, matinee-idol status?

Con. 4: In 1935, Wiley Post was killed in an airplane crash in Alaska. Name the world-famous rope-twirling cowboy humorist who died in the same crash.

3-POINT QUESTIONS

Con. 1: Supply the last names of three great violinists: (a) Jascha, (b) Yehudi, (c) Fritz.

Con. 2: A 1934 spectacle show, staged by Billy Rose, starred Jimmy Durante, Paul Whiteman and several elephants. Name that show.

Con. 3: In 1919 he was just a juggler in Pantages vaudeville. Twenty years later he was radio's top comedian. Name him.

Con. 4: Name two of the three Broadway shows which established the three longest runs on Broadway.

5-POINT QUESTIONS

Con. 1: Who is America's "First Lady of the Stage," and what was her most famous role?

Con. 2: What famous newspaper columnist was once a vaudeville "hoofer"?

Con. 3: Dismissed from St. Mary's Monastery as unsuited for the priesthood, this 16-year-old student turned professional pianist, and within three years became the youngest leader of a popular band on Broadway. Name him.

Con. 4: Name the play Abraham Lincoln was watching when he was shot by John Wilkes Booth.

(Answers on page 145)

ART

Contestant 1: Goya's greatest painting was of a famous duchess. Complete the title of that painting: "Duchess of ...."

Con. 2: Who painted the Sistine Chapel in Rome?

Con. 3: William Hogarth (18th century) was the first important painter of which country?

Con. 4: A portrait of a woman smiling enigmatically, hangs in the Louvre in Paris. It is Leonardo Da Vinci's "La Gioconda." By what other name is it much better known?

3-POINT QUESTIONS

Con. 1: A church erected over the tomb of a great saint has been called the cradle of Italian painting, for its walls contain some of the finest paintings of the early Italian artists (notably Giotto). Name that saint.

Con. 2: Who painted many beautiful Madonnas, including the Madonna of the Chair?

Con. 3: Name the so-called Father of Venetian painting, a school of painting which featured color and formal organization.

Con. 4: Which painter is regarded as having attained the summit of achievement of the Venetian school of painting?

5-POINT QUESTIONS

Con. 1: Name the most powerful of the Italian realist painters of the Renaissance, whose paintings have three-dimensional form of remarkable vigor.

Con. 2: Botticelli loved to indulge his passion for motion in his paintings. One of his great contemporaries had an equal love or passion for featuring light and shade in his work. Name him.

Con. 3: Which two Flemish painters are credited with the invention of a technique in oil varnishes which led to the discovery of true oil painting in the 16th century?

Con. 4: Which German painter, second-rate in all but portraiture, became the court painter for Henry VIII and developed great realism in his portraits?

(Answers on page 145)

People

INVENTORS

Name their principal inventions.

2-POINT QUESTIONS
Contestant 1: Robert Fulton.
Con. 2: Samuel Colt.
Con. 3: Samuel Morse.
Con. 4: George Pullman.

3-POINT QUESTIONS
Con. 1: Cyrus McCormick.
Con. 2: Melville Bissell.
Con. 3: Elisha Otis.
Con. 4: Charles Goodyear.

5-POINT QUESTIONS
Con. 1: Vladimir Zworykin.
Con. 2: Ottmar Mergenthaler.
Con. 3: Elias Howe.
Con. 4: George Westinghouse.

(Answers on page 145)

FAMOUS PEOPLE—Part 1

2-POINT QUESTIONS

Contestant 1: Accused of corrupting the youth of Athens, this Greek philosopher was compelled to drink a poisonous cup of hemlock.

Con. 2: This hated King of England was forced to sign the Magna Carta.

Con. 3: Legend says that a falling apple gave this mathematician the idea of the Law of Gravity.

Con. 4: In silent movie days, she was "America's Sweetheart."

3-POINT QUESTIONS

Con. 1: Who was the "Lady of the Lamp" who founded modern nursing?

Con. 2: This great American poet wrote "Leaves of Grass."

Con. 3: This great Italian sculptor and goldsmith wrote his autobiography.

Con. 4: These twin brothers, from Belgium, became famous for their balloon ascents and bathysphere descents. What is their surname?

5-POINT QUESTIONS

Con. 1: Name the German scientist who discovered X-rays.

Con. 2: This Italian artist often painted hair in a rich red tone.

Con. 3: Name the German socialist who collaborated with Karl Marx in helping complete "Das Kapital."

Con. 4: This military hero of the Mexican war was a bottleneck in the North's Civil War efforts, until Lincoln removed him from his position in November, 1861.

(Answers on page 146)

FAMOUS PEOPLE—Part 2

2-POINT QUESTIONS

Contestant 1: This Macedonian king conquered the entire known world by the time he was 32.

Con. 2: In 1905 he wrote the Theory of Relativity.

Con. 3: This King of England defied the Pope and married Anne Boleyn.

Con. 4: Name the former mining engineer who became the 31st President of our country but lost the 1932 election.

3-POINT QUESTIONS

Con. 1: He was the first Englishman to sail around the world, and in 1588 he defeated the Spanish Armada.

Con. 2: This saint of the Catholic Church founded the Franciscan Order in the 13th century.

Con. 3: The editorial policies of this famous newspaperman helped bring about the Spanish-American War.

Con. 4: After defeating Santa Anna in 1836, this Tennessee soldier-statesman became the first president of the Republic of Texas.

5-POINT QUESTIONS

Con. 1: This Chinese physician turned revolutionary and overthrew the Manchu dynasty, then became the first president of the Chinese Republic.

Con. 2: Name the Prussian general who became an American major-general in the Revolutionary War, and taught our forces drilling and discipline at Valley Forge.

Con. 3: This great French writer detested superstition and fanaticism, and wrote the epic satire "Candide."

Con. 4: The central idea of this Greek philosopher (that number is the principal order of the universe) laid the foundations for the pseudo-science of numerology.

(Answers on page 146)

FAMOUS PEOPLE—Part 3

Contestant 1: This American frontiersman, with little schooling, was three times elected to Congress, then helped Texas in its fight for independence. He was a hero of the Alamo, where he was killed.

Con. 2: From his job as editor of the Nazi newspaper, *Der Angrif,* this spellbinder orator became propaganda minister of the Reich.

Con. 3: As this Egyptian king added weight, he lost popularity and was finally deposed by the army. He fled to exile in Italy.

Con. 4: This Italian traveler journeyed all the way to the court of Kublai Khan in China, starting in 1271 and returning to Venice 24 years later!

Con. 1: This great Austrian expert in neuropathology developed psychoanalysis in the treatment of neurotic disorders and became the Father of Modern Psychiatry.

Con. 2: Name the Greek mathematician who is known as the Father of Geometry. He lived about 300 B.C.

Con. 3: This journalist is best remembered for having said, "Go west, young man, and grow up with the country."

Con. 4: At the age of 15, she married the French prince who later became Louis XVI. At 38, she died beneath the guillotine.

Con. 1: Teddy Roosevelt picked him as the best man to build the Panama Canal—and he finished the job five months ahead of time.

Con. 2: This Russian revolutionist became president of the short-lived Russian republic in 1917, but Lenin and the Bolsheviks overthrew him.

Con. 3: This Roman naturalist was the most famous Roman killed when Mount Vesuvius destroyed the city of Pompeii.

Con. 4: In 18 years as Inquisitor-General, this fanatic put over

2,000 people to death at the stake as "heretics." He was the leading figure of the dreaded Spanish Inquisition.

(Answers on page 146)

FAMOUS PEOPLE—Part 4

2-POINT QUESTIONS

Contestant 1: He is best remembered for his last words: "I regret that I have but one life to lose for my country."

Con. 2: Born a peasant girl at Domremy, France, she became a legendary heroine of her nation as "The Maid of Orleans."

Con. 3: His official title is "King of Kings of Ethiopia, the Conquering Lion of Judah and the Elect of God." His capital is at Addis Ababa.

Con. 4: He faced the Indians fearlessly, but he sent John Alden on a personal mission to Priscilla, rather than face her himself.

3-POINT QUESTIONS

Con. 1: His discovery of gold in the Sacramento Valley of California led to the Gold Rush of 1849; then he died penniless.

Con. 2: This Greek philosopher dramatized his belief in upright, simple living, by carrying a lantern with him "in search of an honest man."

Con. 3: This reformer changed the course of history when he nailed his "95 Propositions" to the door of a church in Wittenberg, Germany.

Con. 4: He made a fortune in tea, and spent a fortune in unsuccessful attempts to lift the America's Cup in yachting.

5-POINT QUESTIONS

Con. 1: She became a heroine of France when she stabbed to death in his bath the infamous Marat of the French Revolution.

Con. 2: This young American naval officer performed "the most daring act of the age" when he burned the frigate *Philadelphia* after it had been captured by the Tripolitanian pirates.

Con. 3: This Persian religious leader conceived the idea of

Good opposing Evil in life, and the "free will" of man to choose between them. He founded a great religion which bore his name.

Con. 4: The chief fame of this British chemist rests on his discovery of oxygen in 1774.

(Answers on page 147)

FAMOUS PEOPLE—Part 5

2-POINT QUESTIONS

Contestant 1: Succeeding to the Presidency upon the death of the incumbent President, this man was sworn into office by his father, at a Vermont farmhouse.

Con. 2: The most famous woman aviator of all time, she disappeared in 1937 on a trip from New Guinea to Howland Island.

Con. 3: He invented the incandescent electric lamp.

Con. 4: She married Napoleon Bonaparte and became the first Empress of the French.

3-POINT QUESTIONS

Con. 1: With African elephants as his "tank corps," he crossed the Alps and brought terror to Rome in 218-217 B.C.

Con. 2: He defended Loeb and Leopold, but his most famous case was his defense of a young science teacher, against prosecution by William Jennings Bryan.

Con. 3: Known as the greatest of all orators, he is said (in legend) to have overcome a speech defect by practicing oratory with pebbles in his mouth!

Con. 4: She was the founder of Christian Science.

5-POINT QUESTIONS

Con. 1: Chosen president of the Turkish Republic in 1923, he performed an astounding job of modernizing that nation.

Con. 2: This American educator's "Eclectic Readers" were standard textbooks in our grade schools for much of the 19th century, and had much to do with shaping American thought in that century.

Con. 3: This French mathematician propounded a theory (the Theory of Probabilities) which became the basis of rate making in the insurance business.

Con. 4: This famous Roman general was first the ally of Julius Caesar but later his political and military enemy. He was defeated at Pharsalus and later assassinated in Egypt.

(Answers on page 147)

FAMOUS PEOPLE—Part 6

2-POINT QUESTIONS

Contestant 1: This sixth President of the United States was the son of a man who had already been our President.

Con. 2: He is generally considered the greatest operatic tenor of all time.

Con. 3: A West Point graduate in 1828, he later joined the secession and became the President of the Confederate States of America.

Con. 4: Which husband-wife team discovered radium?

3-POINT QUESTIONS

Con. 1: A German soldier and story teller, this "Baron" became famous for his "tall tales."

Con. 2: This Swedish chemist invented dynamite, made a fortune on it, then established annual prizes for those who contribute most for mankind's benefit.

Con. 3: Entering the Royal Navy at the age of 12, this man later lost an eye and an arm in sea battles but became Britain's greatest naval hero. Then he lost his life in winning his greatest victory, at Trafalgar.

Con. 4: Known as The Prophet, he founded the Islamic religion.

5-POINT QUESTIONS

Con. 1: This Polish astronomer was the first man to publish

the theory that the planets revolve around the sun, not the sun around the earth.

Con. 2: This former cigar maker became the first president of the American Federation of Labor.

Con. 3: This Portuguese navigator discovered what Columbus had failed to find: the sea route from Europe to India (by way of the Cape of Good Hope).

Con. 4: Rising to fame as an express company detective, this man organized the U. S. Secret Service and was President Lincoln's "guard."

(Answers on page 147)

FAMOUS EXPLORERS

What land or body of water did the following men explore?

2-POINT QUESTIONS

Contestant 1: Vasco de Balboa.

Con. 2: Ponce de Leon.

Con. 3: Hernandes de Soto.

Con. 4: Ferdinand Magellan.

3-POINT QUESTIONS

Con. 1: Hernando Cortez.

Con. 2: Francisco Pizzaro.

Con. 3: Father Jacques Marquette.

Con. 4: John Cabot.

5-POINT QUESTIONS

Con. 1: Francisco de Coronado.

Con. 2: Jacques Cartier.

Con. 3: Sir Walter Raleigh.

Con. 4: Eric the Red.

(Answers on page 147)

SECTION VI

Science

SCIENCE—Part 1

2-POINT QUESTIONS

Contestant 1: One of the three states (conditions or forms) in which matter exists is the solid state. Name the other two.

Con. 2: Name the precious metal which is the most malleable of all metals.

Con. 3: Does sound travel faster in warm or cold air?

Con. 4: From which ore is aluminum made?

Con. 1: When a physicist divides the weight in air of a body heavier than water by the weight in air of an equal volume of water, which property of the first object is he trying to determine?

Con. 2: When two liquids of different concentration are separated by a porous membrane, the liquids tend to pass through the membrane and mix. What is the name of this process?

Con. 3: Why is it impossible for a machine with moving parts to have 100% efficiency?

Con. 4: It is fundamental that energy, though continually changed or transformed, is never destroyed or diminished (although it can be dissipated into an irrecoverable form). What is this principle called?

5-POINT QUESTIONS

Con. 1: Newton's Second Law of Motion holds that the acceleration of a body is in the direction of, and in proportion to, the force that produces it. Describe Newton's First Law of Motion.

Con. 2: Describe Newton's Third Law of Motion.

Con. 3: What is the valence of carbon in most of its compounds?

Con. 4: Which element, contained in all acids, determines the characteristic properties of a particular acid?

(Answers on page 148)

SCIENCE—Part 2

2-POINT QUESTIONS

Contestant 1: In the worship of which two heavenly bodies by the ancient Egyptians and Babylonians did the science of astronomy begin?

Con. 2: What is the instrument called by which atmospheric pressure is commonly measured?

Con. 3: What is the approximate speed of light per second?

Con. 4: Against which dread disease did Edward Jenner develop vaccination?

Con. 1: Which ancient civilization was the first to separate religion from science, in trying to determine the nature of the universe?

Con. 2: Name the Greek doctor who founded the first scientific system of medicine.

Con. 3: Name the famous astronomer of ancient Alexandria, whose theory that the earth was the center of the universe prevailed until disproved by Copernicus.

Con. 4: Name the young professor at Pisa who, according to legend, used the Leaning Tower of Pisa in experiments which disproved the theory Aristotle had propounded, that a heavy body falls faster through space than a light body.

5-POINT QUESTIONS

Con. 1: Name the Greek philosopher who tried to devise one all-embracing system of knowledge which would include everything known to man. His former pupil, Alexander the Great, sent him collections of plants from all over the known world to help him in his study of biology.

Con. 2: Name the French chemist who demonstrated that it is an element in the air (oxygen) which supports combustion.

Con. 3: Name the Austrian priest and botanist who, through his patient experiments crossing and hybridizing many generations of peas, discovered what characteristics are passed on in heredity, and thereby founded the modern science of genetics.

Con. 4: Name the Russian chemist who succeeded in arranging the elements into a comprehensive, periodic table of their atomic weights.

(Answers on page 148)

THE HUMAN BODY

2-POINT QUESTIONS

Contestant 1: In the human body, what do the following have in common: gluteus, maximus, tendo Achillis and triceps?

Con. 2: What do the following have in common: carpus, phalanges, tarsus and clavicle?

Con. 3: In which organ of the body do we find the hammer, anvil and stirrup?

Con. 4: The body takes in and uses oxygen. What gas do the lungs principally give off?

3-POINT QUESTIONS

Con. 1: In what system (general functional part) of the body do we find the pylorus and the duodenum?

Con. 2: In what system (general functional part) of the body do we find the trachea and the epiglottis?

Con. 3: In what system do we find the pons and the medulla oblongata?

Con. 4: Name the largest internal organ of the body.

5-POINT QUESTIONS

Con. 1: How many bones (within 20) are there in the body?

Con. 2: Give a simple explanation of the process of metabolism.

Con. 3: What is tuleremia, and what animal is the principal carrier?

Con.4: The main function of the white corpuscles is to fight infections. What is the major function of the red corpuscles?

(Answers on page 148)

Pot Luck

ABBREVIATIONS

What do these stand for?

2-POINT QUESTIONS

Contestant 1: Mme.
Con. 2: Esq.
Con. 3: Rev.
Con. 4: R.F.D.

3-POINT QUESTIONS

Con. 1: T.N.E.C.
Con. 2: W.P.A.
Con. 3: T.V.A.
Con. 4. U.S.S.R.

5-POINT QUESTIONS

Con. 1: S.H.A.E.F.
Con. 2: S.H.A.P.E.
Con. 3: U.N.R.R.A.
Con. 4: U.N.E.S.C.O.

(Answers on page 149)

POT LUCK—Part 1

Contestant 1: Sitting Bull led the Indian forces which annihilated the cavalry troop of General Custer on June 25, 1876. Of which great Indian tribe was he a member?

Con. 2: Is "Solon" famous as the name of a planet, a foreign-make automobile or an Athenian lawmaker?

Con. 3: The Japanese call this movie character Miki Kuchi; the French call him Michel Souris; and in Sweden he is known as Musse Pig. What is his name in this country?

Con. 4: To "rook" is a slang term meaning to steal from, but in which popular game is a rook used?

3-POINT QUESTIONS

Con. 1: The Phoenician wife of King Ahab of Israel was a cruel and willful woman. She favored the idolatrous worship of Baal and persecuted the prophets of Jehovah. What was her name?

Con. 2: Which President of the United States coined the now-famous expression, "To the victor belong the spoils"?

Con. 3: In our own Solar System, which planet is nearest the Sun?

Con. 4: In many parts of the world, especially Asia, people still use a counting device that goes back before recorded history. It is a board with beads on it. What is this primitive "Univac" called?

5-POINT QUESTIONS

Con. 1: What is the square root of .09?

Con. 2: According to the Bible, one of Noah's descendants was a mighty hunter. His name is frequently used to denote a successful hunter. Can you give us that name?

Con. 3: In Salisbury Plain, England, there is a group of ancient stone circles believed to have been temples of the Druids over 4,000 years ago. What is that group of historic ruins called?

Con. 4: The ancient Greeks dedicated a temple to Athena at Athens which is regarded as the finest example of Grecian architecture. It has been called "the one perfect thing created by the hand of man." Can you name that great temple?

(Answers on page 149)

POT LUCK—Part 2

2-POINT QUESTIONS

Contestant 1: One of the colorful figures of the Gay Nineties was a former newsboy who, on July 23, 1886, allegedly "took a chance" and jumped off the Brooklyn Bridge and survived. What was his name?

Con. 2: In what war did the future General Grant and the future General Lee serve on the same side?

Con. 3: What was the name of the Governor of New York who bought the Island of Manhattan from the Indians for $24?

Con. 4: In Greek mythology, a woman opened a box Zeus had commanded her to leave closed. She thereby loosed trouble in its many forms upon the world. What was her name?

3-POINT QUESTIONS

Con. 1: Which book of the New Testament was written by a physician?

Con. 2: An expression has crept into the English language which means to be obsequious to, to acknowledge the superiority of another, or to flatter another. The expression is kow-tow. In which language did it originate?

Con. 3: In the song "Comin' Thru the Rye," is the reference to rye meant as a river, a field of grain or a bottle?

Con. 4: A lot of "westerns" we see on television contain references to a crackshot woman of the pioneer west called "Calamity Jane." Was she a real or a fictitious person?

5-POINT QUESTIONS

Con. 1: In 1844, Congress granted Samuel Morse the money to establish the first long-distance telegraph lines. The following year the 11th President was elected, the first President to learn of his election by telegraph. Can you name him?

Con. 2: When she was a child, this girl's mother was executed by order of her father, who practically ignored the child thereafter. Nevertheless, the child later came to the throne and survived many plots against her life and reign. She ruled a great nation for 45 years. What was her name?

Con. 3: Natives of the far Pacific, off the coast of Asia, have taught a large bird (which cannot fly) to stand in shallow waters and catch fish. Can you name that bird?

Con. 4: Within two pounds, state how much a cubic foot of water weighs.

(Answers on page 150)

POT LUCK—Part 3

2-POINT QUESTIONS

Contestant 1: Name the author and the play (a tragedy) from which came the world-famous expression about something being rotten in Denmark.

Con. 2: A Maryland preacher, named Parson Mason Weems, wrote a book titled "The Life of George Washington," in which the good parson told a little lie about Washington that has become an accepted legend about him. Can you identify that legend about an event that never really happened?

Con. 3: Which great American general (later one of our Presidents) was captured by the British and held as a prisoner of war although he was only 14 years of age? He later avenged that imprisonment by giving them their worst defeat of the War of 1812.

Con. 4: Here is an inscription on a famous statue: "Send these, the homeless, tempest-tossed to me. I lift my lamp beside the golden door!" Can you name that statue?

3-POINT QUESTIONS

Con. 1: Edmund Burke once described the clergy, the nobility, and the mass of the people as "three estates of mankind." Then he pointed to a group of men attending a meeting of the British Parliament and said, "Yonder sits the Fourth Estate, more powerful than the others." Whom did he mean by the Fourth Estate?

Con. 2: Is a bat (the flying variety) more closely related, biologically, to a bird, a butterfly or a cow?

Con. 3: We know that the Democratic Party is symbolized by a donkey, and the Republicans by an elephant; but which political party of 1912 was known as the Bull Moose Party and who was its candidate for the Presidency?

Con. 4: We know what a ringmaster is in a circus, but do you know what a bushmaster is?

5-POINT QUESTIONS

Con. 1: There is an historical legend which says General Grant received General Lee's sword (but returned it) in a token of the South's capitulation at Appomattox Courthouse. Is that legend true or false?

Con. 2: New York City was settled in 1624. St. Louis was first settled in 1764. Can you name the oldest city of the United States?

Con. 3: Most green plants get their food from a chemical process for which sunlight provides the energy. What is that process called?

Con. 4: Which famous Italian poet, heading a small number of troops, seized Fiume for Italy in 1919? Later, his fiery eloquence helped found the Fascist Party.

(Answers on page 150)

POT LUCK—Part 4

2-POINT QUESTIONS

Contestant 1: The official residence of our President is called the White House because it was painted white after its walls were blackened by fire when the British set it ablaze in 1814. But who was the American President (famous as a "Rough Rider") who gave it that name?

Con. 2: In the story "Gone With The Wind," which Southern city was burned to the ground?

Con. 3: The Titanic was sunk by an iceberg. What sank the Lusitania?

Con. 4: Professional soldiers were hired by England to fight in the American Revolution. By what name were they known?

3-POINT QUESTIONS

Con. 1: Our regular house thermometers are based on the Fahrenheit calibration method and show the freezing point of water at 32 degrees. What is water's freezing point under the Centigrade calibration method?

Con. 2: Which two legendary children, who are later said to have founded Rome, were saved from death and nursed by a female wolf?

Con. 3: Only one of the great cities of the world is situated on two different continents. Can you give either its old or its new name?

Con. 4: Brazil is the largest republic of South America. Can you name the smallest?

5-POINT QUESTIONS

Con. 1: What are the common names for these medical terms: (1) caries, (2) myopia, (3) missing patellar reflex?

Con. 2: In Shakespeare's plays, which famous king found himself in such need for a horse, that he'd have swapped his kingdom for one?

Con. 3: In 1929 a British doctor observed a moldy growth from which penicillin was discovered. What was that eminent doctor's name?

Con. 4: In which war did the "Black Death" play an important part—the Crimean War, World War II, the Mexican War, or The Hundred Years War?

(Answers on page 151)

POT LUCK—Part 5

Contestant 1: What is the largest and most important river in Alaska, which has given its name to an entire region there?

Con. 2: Who was famous, in the folklore of American music, for minding the music and being quite handy with the girls?

Con. 3: Which famous American said, "Early to bed and early to rise, makes a man healthy, wealthy, and wise"?

Con. 4: Under which British ruler was Benjamin Disraeli the Prime Minister of England?

3-POINT QUESTIONS

Con. 1: Which is the most brilliant planet of our solar system?

Con. 2: Auguste Rodin (1840-1917) was the greatest French sculptor of modern times. What is the name of his famous statue of a male figure?

Con. 3: At which university is the "Hall of Fame" located?

Con. 4: Which Captain of the French Army was falsely convicted of selling military secrets, sent to Devil's Island, but later exonerated and made a major?

5-POINT QUESTIONS

Con. 1: Name the Secretary of War who, when Abraham Lincoln died, said, "Now he belongs to the ages!"

Con. 2: The machine gun is an American invention, no matter what the Russians claim. Can you name the man who produced the first true machine gun, in the 1860's?

Con. 3: At the Battle of Syracuse, a Greek mathematician employed curved mirror surfaces to concentrate the sun's rays on the attacking Roman ships and set them afire. Can you name that great mathematician?

Con. 4: Who was the famous general who said to his troops, "From the summit of yonder pyramids, forty centuries look down upon you!"?

(Answers on page 151)

POT LUCK—Part 6

Contestant 1: Which two famous rivers combine to form the longest river system in the world?

Con. 2: Paul Revere arranged to receive certain lantern signals from the tower of the Old North Church. In which city was that church situated?

Con. 3: Is the song "London Bridge Is Falling Down" based on fact or fancy?

Con. 4: In Dickens' "Tale of Two Cities," which two great European capitals are involved?

3-POINT QUESTIONS

Con. 1: In which Italian town did Stradivari make his violins?

Con. 2: The International Date Line is an imaginary date line in the Pacific Ocean area. If you cross it going from East to West, do you add or subtract a day from your calendar reckonings?

Con. 3: Which famous woman, a bride of a Sultan, had to keep thinking up interesting stories to save her life?

Con. 4: Name the girl from New Salem, Ill., whose sudden death in 1835 was a source of great grief to Lincoln.

5-POINT QUESTIONS

Con. 1: What does the motto "E Pluribus Unum" mean and who suggested it as a motto for the United States?

Con. 2: One of the most dramatic episodes of World War II occurred in December 1939 when a German pocket battleship was sunk by a British naval force. Can you name that battleship?

Con. 3: What was the name of the second wife of Julius Caesar, of whom it was said, "Caesar's wife must be above suspicion"?

Con. 4: Identify these famous people who are a part of the history of the Old West: (1) A frontierswoman who lived in Deadwood. Some say she earned her nickname when 11 of her 12 husbands died; (2) a frontier marshall and scout for the Army, who was murdered in Deadwood in 1876.

(Answers on page 152)

POT LUCK—Part 7

Contestant 1: On May 6, 1937, there occurred a disaster at Lakehurst, N. J., which practically ended military and civilian aviation interest in "lighter than air" craft (dirigibles). What was that disaster?

Con. 2: Can you name the largest seaport in Alabama? It has a beautiful bay, made famous in a popular song written in 1910.

Con. 3: A definite law of nature should help you answer this one. Which has the highest rate of pulse—an elephant or a mouse?

Con. 4: In the Bible, Cain is noted for his anger, but who is renowned for his patience?

3-POINT QUESTIONS

Con. 1: Which grandson of Queen Victoria once led a nation in a bitter war against England? He was the son of her eldest daughter, Vicky.

Con. 2: There are many famous cities in Texas, but the shrine of The Alamo is as famous as the city in which it is situated. Can you name that city?

Con. 3: George Washington is known as the Father of his Country, but another President is sometimes called the Father of the University of Virginia. Name him.

Con. 4: Catherine de Medici had certain rooms of the Louvre so constructed, that by means of tubes called auriculaires, what was said in one room could easily be heard in another. This gave rise to an expression in our language, cautioning people about indiscreet talk. What is that expression?

5-POINT QUESTIONS

Con. 1: The word "phillipic" means a severe scolding, a speech full of invective. Name the Greek orator whose speeches gave rise to this word, and the king against whom they were delivered.

Con. 2: Franklin D. Roosevelt served longest as U. S. President. Which President served for the shortest period of time?

Con. 3: The biggest mammal in the world feeds on a minute form of sea life. Name the mammal and its food.

Con. 4: Two months before Lee surrendered at Appomattox, President Lincoln boarded the Union transport "River Queen," to meet with three men named Stevens, Hunter and Campbell. Tell (a) whom the three men represented; (b) the purpose of the meeting; and (c) why the meeting failed.

(Answers on page 152)

POT LUCK—Part 8

2-POINT QUESTIONS

Contestant 1: In Tennyson's poem, "Locksley Hall," this line appears: "In the Spring a livelier iris changes on the burnished dove." What is the very famous line that follows it?

Con. 2: Why did a guest fear to drink a glass of wine with Cesare Borgia and his sister, Lucrezia?

Con. 3: There is a lot of speculation now on travelling to the moon in the near future. How far is the moon from the earth: 55,000 miles, 239,000 miles, 1 million miles, or 1,000 meters?

Con. 4: There have been many famous, individual baseball players, but for what was the combination of "Tinker to Evers to Chance" noted?

3-POINT QUESTIONS

Con. 1: Modern warfare involves complex mathematical formulas. However, in World War I, what did the numbers "40 and 8" mean to a doughboy in France?

Con. 2: We all know what a "defendant" is, but can you describe the relationship of being an "accessory before the fact"?

Con. 3: In 37 A.D., Nero, one of the cruelest rulers of all time, was born at an Italian village near the Tiber estuary. On January 22, 1944, the Allied forces established a beachhead there in some of the cruelest fighting of World War II. Name that village.

Con. 4: In Greek mythology, nectar was the drink of the gods. What was the name of the fabulous food they had which gave them strength, power, beauty and immortality?

Con. 1: Give the popular nicknames given by the Air Force to the following airplanes used in World War II: the P-40, P-47, P-51 and the B-24.

Con. 2: Which states would you visit if you visited the sites of the following battles of our history: (1) Vicksburg, (2) Ticonderoga, (3) Tippecanoe, (4) Little Big Horn?

Con. 3: What important engagement of the Civil War was known as "The Battle Above the Clouds"?

Con. 4: What lovely Canadian city is called The City of the Saints and why?

(Answers on page 153)

POT LUCK—Part 9

2-POINT QUESTIONS

Contestant 1: In a fairy tale, a funny little man with a long name helped a girl spin straw into gold. What was his name?

Con. 2: The phrase "dead as a dodo" is often used humorously. Was the dodo an actual bird or a mythical one?

Con. 3: As long ago as 1230 A.D., rockets were used to win a decisive battle. Which Asiatic country used them?

Con. 4: The U. S. Navy has had many famous ships, but a fictional Navy ship, commanded by Captain Queeg, is also known to millions. Can you name it?

3-POINT QUESTIONS

Con. 1: Name Alexander the Great's father, whose assassination put young Alexander on the throne.

Con. 2: Identify the Presidents during whose campaigns the following slogans were used:

(1) A chicken in every pot; a car in every garage;

(2) He kept us out of war;

(3) Tippecanoe and Tyler, too.

Con. 3: The word "cleave" is one of the few words in our language to have two quite opposite meanings. Give both meanings.

Con. 4: With which important Oriental religion are the Analects associated?

5-POINT QUESTIONS

Con. 1: In 1888 the man who got the most popular votes in the election didn't become our President because his opponent got the majority of the electoral votes. Name those two candidates and their parties.

Con. 2: What gluttonous seabird is used by the native Chinese to catch fish, which it is then forced to disgorge from its beak?

Con. 3: A stone found in 1799 by a French officer contained inscriptions in three ancient languages. Because one of those languages was Greek, it enabled scholars to translate the previously unknown hieroglyphic language of Egypt. Can you name the famous stone?

Con. 4: In 1839 the "Great Western" and "The Sirius" revolutionized transportation. Tell how.

(Answers on page 153)

POT LUCK—Part 10

2-POINT QUESTIONS

Con. 1: Which British Prime Minister, famed for carrying an umbrella, promised the world "peace in our time"?

Con. 2: Are gargoyles (1) leprechauns, (2) grotesque figures on buildings, or (3) throat medications?

Con. 3: The followers of which profession take the "Oath of Hippocrates"?

Con. 4: In the famous Mark Twain stories, what was the name of Tom Sawyer's pretty girl-friend?

3-POINT QUESTIONS

Con. 1: General Washington was our first general who became President; General Eisenhower, the latest. Name these generals who also became President: a general whose decisive victory at New

Orleans made him the military hero of the War of 1812; a general who defeated Santa Anna at Buena Vista in 1847.

Con. 2: Paul Bunyan was a legendary hero of the lumber camps. It is said he dug the Grand Canyon just by carelessly dragging his pick behind him. He had an equally famous pet ox. What was its name?

Con. 3: Of all the states which border the oceans along the coast line of the U. S., which has the shortest coast line?

Con. 4: When the Spanish explorer, Grellana, discovered a large river in South America (1541), he thought he saw fierce women warriors on its banks. He therefore named the river after a race of female warriors who the ancient Greeks thought lived in Scythia. Name that river.

5-POINT QUESTIONS

Con. 1: There are six visible colors in the ordinary spectrum. Name any five.

Con. 2: Name the Polish-born novelist who became an officer in the British merchant marine, and later wrote such great books as "An Outcast of the Islands."

Con. 3: We remember a certain King of Epirus because, after a very costly victory over the Romans at Asculum, he said that one more such victory and he would be undone. What was his name?

Con. 4: In which church in which Italian city is Leonardo da Vinci's frescoe, "The Last Supper"?

(Answers on page 154)

POT LUCK—Part 11

2-POINT QUESTIONS

Contestant 1: Descended from the mammoth, the elephant is the largest land mammal. Which is bigger—the African elephant or the Indian elephant?

Con. 2: What is the center of a whirlpool called?

Con. 3: 150 years ago a famous man crowned himself Emperor.

He performed the rites himself because he said that no other man was great enough to crown him. Who was that Emperor?

Con. 4: How much of the earth's surface is covered by water— 25%, 50% or 71%?

3-POINT QUESTIONS

Con. 1: In Greek mythology, who ruled the underworld?

Con. 2: Can you name the President of the U. S. who married a woman only to find, two years later, that her divorce from her first husband was invalid?

Con. 3: When Julius Caesar was assassinated, a beautiful young queen, who had accompanied him to Rome two years before, returned to her native land. But her beauty so beguiled Caesar's best friend, that he went to war with his brother-in-law, Octavian, over her. Name that queen and her defender.

Con. 4: Name the inventor in the field of communications, who gave the Almighty full credit for his invention, by sending this question as its first message: "What hath God wrought?"

5-POINT QUESTIONS

Con. 1: For uncounted centuries, seals have found their way to a group of islands in the Bering Sea to raise their young. Can you name those islands?

Con. 2: Europe and our own continent might have had an Oriental culture today, had it not been for a Greek general who persuaded the Athenians to build a navy as a defense, against the Persians under Xerxes. In 480 B.C., this great Athenian defeated the Persian navy at the Battle of Salamis and thereby changed the course of history. What was his name?

Con. 3: With the relatively primitive equipment available to him during our Civil War, a photographer nevertheless left hundreds of photos of that war which are still regarded as masterpieces. Who was that photographer?

Con. 4: A furor was created in England on Christmas Day, 1950, when which famous object, involving the history of England and Scotland, was stolen from Westminster Abbey?

(Answers on page 154)

POT LUCK—Part 12

Contestant 1: Who is the famous king renowned in song as loving his tobacco, his food and music?

Con. 2: For hundreds of years men pursued it. What were they after when they sought the "Northwest Passage"?

Con. 3: Which long and lanky movie star played the part of Lou Gehrig in the movie "Pride of the Yankees"?

Con. 4: When an athlete performs the "squeeze play" successfully, is he participating in baseball, cricket or wrestling?

3-POINT QUESTIONS

Con. 1: What member of the bird family avoids its egg-sitting responsibilities by laying its eggs in the nests of other birds?

Con. 2: Venice was built on a group of islands to discourage invasion, but which other big European city was built on hundreds of islands in order to claim land from the sea?

Con. 3: Prior to World War II, France foolishly put its trust in the Maginot Line, which the Germans outflanked. Can you name the "line" of fortresses the Germans depended on, but which the Allies smashed through?

Con. 4: In Gene Tunney's 61 professional fights, he lost only one decision—to a tough scrapper from Pittsburgh. Who held that decision over Tunney?

5-POINT QUESTIONS

Con. 1: Many well-known people have been held for ransom by kidnappers, but name the most famous of them all—the man who later became a famous Roman general but who, earlier in life, was captured by pirates and held for a ransom equaling $125,000.

Con. 2: With the early history of which state was each of the following famous colonial-day figures connected: General James Oglethorpe, Captain John Smith, Increase Mather?

Con. 3: During the Civil War, army deserters were commonly called "mossbacks." Why?

Con. 4: If you took a steamboat at Cairo, Ill., and sailed down

(Answers on page 155)

to New Orleans, La., name the five other states along whose boundaries you would travel.

POT LUCK—Part 13

Contestant 1: In 1858, a famous Indian warrior swore revenge on the settlers of the Southwest after his wife and children had been killed by Mexicans. In World War II, our paratroopers adopted this chief's name as their war cry. What was that name?

Con. 2: When Roman citizens appeared in public, they wore a loose outer garment made of a semicircular piece of cloth. Name that garment.

Con. 3: Five-foot-four Stephen Douglas was known as "The Little Orator" of American politics. Which physical giant of a man did he face in a series of debates in 1858?

Con. 4: When Cortez reached Mexico, he found an Indian civilization whose culture and learning exceeded anything he had expected to find in the New World. Which Indians were they?

3-POINT QUESTIONS

Con. 1: In April 1933, a motorist driving along the shore of a lake in Scotland, saw a marine monster for which circuses have offered a price of $100,000 if caught alive. It is thought to be a survival from prehistoric times. Can you give the name of that monster as given by the press?

Con. 2: Can you name the great comet which flashed within view of the earth in 1910? Millions of people thought it presaged the end of the world.

Con. 3: In the 1840's, a Texas rancher refused to brand his cattle. Today his name has become a word signifying a motherless calf (or in a broader sense, any homeless thing). What is that word?

Con. 4: Is a "Janizary" a rare bird, a Roman temple dedicated to the God Janus, or a member of the Sultan's guard?

Con. 1: This King of Babylon, to please his wife, who complained about the flatness of the country, built one of the Seven Wonders of the World. He died in 562 B.C. Can you name him?

Con. 2: Here are the names of 10 generals who fought in the Civil War. Pick out those who fought for the North as distinguished from those who fought for the South: Burnside, Jackson, Lee, Custer, Buckner, McClellan, Longstreet, Grant, Kearny and Hampton.

Con. 3: In the 18th century, a great English navigator discovered a Pacific paradise which he named the Sandwich Islands. We now call it Hawaii. Who was that navigator?

Con. 4: We are told that Noah sent forth two birds from the Ark to see if land had reappeared. The one that returned was a dove. What kind of bird was the other?

(Answers on page 155)

SPELLING TEST—Part 1

(Enough words are provided in this quiz for three rounds among four contestants.)

2-POINT WORDS

Con. 1: bleach	despair	theirs
Con. 2: cruise	despise	thief
Con. 3: lining	different	idiot
Con. 4: lullaby	crumble	frequent

3-POINT WORDS

Con. 1: changeable	achieve	development
Con. 2: chivalrous	acrimony	dictionary
Con. 3: deceitful	mackerel	dilapidated
Con. 4: deterrent	blasphemous	dilatory

5-POINT WORDS

Con. 1: bouillon	diaphragm	narcissism
Con. 2: conscientious	crustacean	nauseous
Con. 3: chauffeur	dilettante	notoriety
Con. 4: meretricious	timorous	laryngeal

(THESE ARE THE CORRECT SPELLINGS. THERE IS NO ANSWER PAGE FOR THIS QUIZ.)

SPELLING TEST—Part 2

(Enough words are provided in this quiz for three rounds among four contestants.)

2-POINT WORDS

Con. 1: create	reverse	salve
Con. 2: recoil	rouse	session
Con. 3: reign	penance	cannibal
Con. 4: resume	retrieve	actual

3-POINT WORDS

Con. 1: execrable	moccasin	adrenalin
Con. 2: inseparable	obsequious	bacchanal
Con. 3: witticism	demeanor	miscellaneous
Con. 4: symmetry	reminisce	tourniquet

5-POINT WORDS

Con. 1: sacrilegious	anachronism	excrescence
Con. 2: chrysanthemum	apocryphal	chrysalis
Con. 3: transcendental	calumniate	synthesize
Con. 4: phantasmagoria	entrepreneur	sanguinary

(THESE ARE THE CORRECT SPELLINGS. THERE IS NO ANSWER PAGE FOR THIS QUIZ.)

SPELLING TEST—Part 3

(Enough words are provided in this quiz for three rounds among four contestants.)

2-POINT WORDS

Con. 1: dissolve	receipt	dessert
Con. 2: domain	rapture	poach
Con. 3: statue	crackle	process
Con. 4: ladle	prisoner	pumpkin

3-POINT WORDS

Con. 1: discipline	epidemic	meteorology
Con. 2: massacre	parallel	unguent
Con. 3: piteous	stoically	sabotage
Con. 4: ominous	obedience	sacrificial

5-POINT WORDS

Con. 1: mayonnaise	metamorphosis	maraschino
Con. 2: peripatetic	parliamentary	tonsillectomy
Con. 3: presumptuous	obeisance	trousseau
Con. 4: ptomaine	psychoanalysis	nascent

(THESE ARE THE CORRECT SPELLINGS. THERE IS NO ANSWER PAGE FOR THIS QUIZ.)

Answers

GENERAL LITERATURE—Part 1

2-POINT QUESTIONS: Con. 1: "Gone With The Wind." Con. 2: Rudyard Kipling. Con. 3: "The Legend of Sleepy Hollow." Con. 4: "Black Beauty."

3-POINT QUESTIONS: Con. 1: Edgar Allan Poe. Con. 2: That the murderer had written the German word for revenge. Con. 3: Beau Brummel (real). Lady Godiva (real). George Babbitt (fictional—in Sinclair Lewis' novel). Cyrano de Bergerac (fictional—Edmond Rostand's play). Minnehaha (fictional—Longfellow's poem). Copernicus (real). Con. 4: Carl Sandburg.

5-POINT QUESTIONS: Con. 1: Robin Hood (who was allegedly born in Locksley, in Nottinghamshire, in the 12th century). Con. 2: "Gulliver's Travels," which satirizes the faults of mankind through the Lilliputians and the Brobdingnagians). Con. 3: Dante's great love was Beatrice (Portinari). Con. 4: The Fallen Angel was Satan; his children, Sin and Death.

GENERAL LITERATURE—Part 2

2-POINT QUESTIONS: Con. 1: "Kidnapped." Con. 2: Jules Verne. Con. 3: King Arthur. Con. 4: Sherlock Holmes.

3-POINT QUESTIONS: Con. 1: "Utopia." Con. 2: "Pilgrim's Progress," an allegory based on the adventures of Christian on his way from the City of Destruction to the Celestial City. Con. 3: "Don Quixote." Con. 4: Eugene O'Neill.

5-POINT QUESTIONS: Con. 1: Mrs. Malaprop. Con. 2: "Robinson Crusoe" by Daniel Defoe. Con. 3: (a) George Eliot (Mary Ann Evans), (b) Jane Austen, (c) Jan Struther. Con. 4: "Ulysses" by James Joyce.

GENERAL LITERATURE—Part 3

2-POINT QUESTIONS: Con. 1: Oliver Twist. Con. 2: Aesop. Con. 3: Gilbert and Sullivan. Con. 4: "Beware the Ides of March" (March 15).

3-POINT QUESTIONS: Con. 1: Abou Ben Adhem (in Leigh Hunt's poem). Con. 2: Enoch Arden. Con. 3: Edgar Allan Poe's "The Gold Bug." Con. 4: The Elizabethan Age.

5-POINT QUESTIONS: Con. 1: "The House of the Seven Gables." Con. 2: "Il Penseroso" and "L'Allegro." Con. 3: Bassanio chose the lead casket. Con. 4: "Strange Interlude."

GENERAL LITERATURE—Part 4

2-POINT QUESTIONS: Con. 1: O. Henry. Con. 2: The Ancient Mariner of Coleridge's poem of that title: "Water, water everywhere; nor any drop to drink." Con. 3: Dr. Fu Manchu. Con. 4: The series that began with "Tarzan of the Apes."

3-POINT QUESTIONS: Con. 1: "The Sea Wolf" (Jack London). Con. 2: "Ivanhoe" (Sir Walter Scott). Con. 3: Gopher Prairie. Con. 4: Grover's Corners.

5-POINT QUESTIONS: Con. 1: Jefferson. Con. 2: (a) Mexico. (b) Poland. Con. 3: (a) Peru. (b) France. Con. 4: (a) Pantagruel. (b) Gargantua.

AMERICAN AUTHORS

2-POINT QUESTIONS: Con. 1: Mark Twain. Con. 2: "The Call of the Wild." Con. 3: "An American Tragedy." Con. 4: "Babbitt."

3-POINT QUESTIONS: Con. 1: "The Luck of Roaring Camp." Con. 2: Joel Chandler Harris. Con. 3: Stephen Crane. Con. 4: "The Jungle."

5-POINT QUESTIONS: F. Scott Fitzgerald. Con. 2: "Studs Lonigan." Con. 3: Jean Francois Millet. Con. 4: Theodore Roosevelt.

SHAKESPEARE

2-POINT QUESTIONS: Con. 1: "Julius Caesar." Con. 2: "Macbeth." Con. 3: "The Taming of the Shrew." Con. 4: "Romeo and Juliet."

3-POINT QUESTIONS: Con. 1: "King Henry VI (Part I)." Con. 2: "Love's Labour Lost." Con. 3: "A Midsummer-Night's Dream." Con. 4: "The Tempest."

5-POINT QUESTIONS: Con. 1: Octavia. Con. 2: Lady Anne. Con. 3: Viola. Con. 4: Bianca.

NAME THE POEM (OR PLAY)—Part 1

2-POINT QUESTIONS: Con. 1: "Rime of the Ancient Mariner" (Coleridge). Con. 2: "Old Ironsides" (Oliver Wendell Holmes). Con. 3: "Charge of the Light Brigade" (Tennyson). Con. 4: "Romeo and Juliet" (Shakespeare).

3-POINT QUESTIONS: Con. 1: "The Ballad of Reading Gaol" (Oscar Wilde). Con. 2: "Break, Break, Break" (Tennyson). Con. 3: "Abou Ben Adhem" (Leigh Hunt). Con. 4: "Sonnets from the Portuguese (Elizabeth Barrett Browning).

5-POINT QUESTIONS: Con. 1: "A Psalm of Life" (Longfellow). Con. 2: "An Incident of the French Camp" (Browning). Con. 3: "As You Like It" (Shakespeare). Con. 4: "Burial of Sir John Moore at Corunna" (Charles Wolfe).

NAME THE POEM (OR PLAY)—Part 2

2-POINT QUESTIONS: Con. 1: "The Raven" (Edgar Allan Poe). Con. 2: "Barbara Frietchie" (Whittier). Con. 3: "Gunga Din" (Kipling). Con. 4: "Crossing the Bar" (Tennyson).

3-POINT QUESTIONS: Con. 1: "She Walks in Beauty" (Lord Byron). Con. 2: "The Vampire" (Kipling). Con. 3: "The Rubaiyat'" (Omar Khayyam). Con. 4: "In Flanders Fields" (John McCrae).

5-POINT QUESTIONS: Con. 1: "O Captain! My Captain!" (Walt Whitman). Con. 2: "Chicago" (Carl Sandburg). Con. 3: "The Fool's Prayer" (Edward R. Sill). Con. 4: "The Highwayman" (Alfred Noyes).

"BAD GUYS" (of Life and Literature)—Part 1

2-POINT QUESTIONS: Con. 1: Frankenstein's Monster. Con. 2: John Dillinger. Con. 3: Mr. Hyde. Con. 4: Al Capone.

3-POINT QUESTIONS: Con. 1: William Bligh. Con. 2: Macbeth. Con. 3: Mephistopheles. Con. 4: Rasputin.

5-POINT QUESTIONS: Con. 1: Billy the Kid. Con. 2: Heydrich the Hangman (Reichsprotektor Reinhard Heydrich). Con. 3: Blackbeard. Con. 4: Israel Hands.

"BAD GUYS" (of Life and Literature)—Part 2

2-POINT QUESTIONS: Con. 1: Nero. Con. 2: Sitting Bull. Con. 3: Scrooge. Con. 4: Attila.

3-POINT QUESTIONS: Con. 1: Iago. Con. 2: Jean Lafitte. Con. 3: Fagin. Con. 4: The Devil.

5-POINT QUESTIONS: Con. 1: Javert. Con. 2: General Zaroff. Con. 3: Niccolo Machiavelli. Con. 4: The Duke of Alva.

WHO WROTE IT?

2-POINT QUESTIONS: Con. 1: Harriet Beecher Stowe. Con. 2: Ernest Hemingway. Con. 3: Louisa May Alcott. Con. 4: Charles Dickens.

3-POINT QUESTIONS: Con. 1: Mark Twain. Con. 2: Elizabeth Barrett Browning. Con. 3: Herman Melville. Con. 4: H. G. Wells.

5-POINT QUESTIONS: Con. 1: Thomas De Quincey. Con. 2: Edgar Allan Poe. Con. 3: James Boswell. Con. 4: Richard Henry Dana.

AUTHOR'S MOST FAMOUS WORK—Part 1

2-POINT QUESTIONS: Con. 1: "The Odyssey" or "The Iliad." Con. 2: "Songs of Solomon." Con. 3: The Declaration of Independence. Con. 4: "Poor Richard's Almanac" or "Autobiography."

3-POINT QUESTIONS: Con. 1: His diary. Con. 2: "The Decameron." Con. 3: "Canterbury Tales." Con. 4: "The Compleat Angler."

5-POINT QUESTIONS: Con. 1: "Tom Jones." Con. 2: "The Divine Comedy." Con. 3: "Imitation of Christ." Con. 4: "Wealth of Nations."

AUTHOR'S MOST FAMOUS WORK—Part 2

2-POINT QUESTIONS: Con. 1: "20,000 Leagues under the Sea." Con. 2: "Moby Dick." Con. 3: "Uncle Tom's Cabin." Con. 4: "Les Miserables."

3-POINT QUESTION: Con. 1: "The Man without a Country." Con. 2: "Four Horsemen of the Apocalypse." Con. 3: "Silas

Marner" or "Mill on the Floss." Con. 4: "Two Years before the Mast."

5-POINT QUESTIONS: Con. 1: "The Oregon Trail." Con. 2: "Vanity Fair." Con. 3: "Jane Eyre." Con. 4: "Wuthering Heights."

AUTHOR'S MOST FAMOUS WORK—Part 3

2-POINT QUESTIONS: Con. 1: "The Good Earth." Con. 2: "All Quiet on the Western Front." Con. 3: "An American Tragedy." Con. 4: "Trees."

3-POINT QUESTIONS: "The Robe." Con. 2: "The Red Badge of Courage." Con. 3: "Main Street," "Babbitt," or "Arrowsmith." Con. 4: "Anthony Adverse."

5-POINT QUESTIONS: Con. 1: "Jurgen." Con. 2: "Cyrano de Bergerac." Con. 3: Oedipus Rex." Con. 4: "The Faerie Queene."

AUTHOR'S MOST FAMOUS WORK—Part 4

2-POINT QUESTIONS: Con. 1: "Adventures of Sherlock Holmes." Con. 2: "Treasure Island." Con. 3: "Little Women." Con. 4: "Alice in Wonderland."

3-POINT QUESTIONS: Con. 1: "The Blue Bird." Con. 2: "The Man With the Hoe." Con. 3: "The Luck of Roaring Camp." Con. 4: "The Brothers Karamazov," or "Crime and Punishment."

5-POINT QUESTIONS: Con. 1: "The Red and the Black." Con. 2: "Tess of the d'Urbervilles." Con. 3: "Madame Bovary." Con. 4: "The Republic."

COUPLE THE COUPLES—Part 1

2-POINT QUESTIONS: Con. 1: John Alden. Con. 2: Pocahontas. Con. 3: Scarlett O'Hara. Con. 4: Lady Hamilton.

3-POINT QUESTIONS: Con. 1: Prince Albert. Con. 2: Elizabeth Barrett. Con. 3: Chopin. Con. 4: Heloise.

5-POINT QUESTIONS: Con. 1: King Henry II. Con. 2: Aspasia. Con. 3: Jane Eyre. Con. 4: Captain Macheath.

COUPLE THE COUPLES—Part 2

2-POINT QUESTIONS: Con. 1: Cleopatra. Con. 2: Maid Marian.
Con. 3: Helen of Troy. Con. 4: Bath-sheba.

3-POINT QUESTIONS: Con. 1: Sir Launcelot. Con. 2: Isolde.
Con. 3: Leander. Con. 4: Juno.

5-POINT QUESTIONS: Con. 1: Gabriel. Con. 2: Fair Ellen. Con.
3: Cressida. Con. 4: Josephine.

FAMOUS SAYINGS—Part 1

2-POINT QUESTIONS: Con. 1: Mae West. Con. 2: Duke of
Windsor, King Edward VIII, in his farewell broadcast. Con. 3:
Woodrow Wilson. Con. 4: Harry S. Truman.

3-POINT QUESTIONS: Con. 1: Franklin D. Roosevelt. Con. 2:
Tony Galento (about any opponent). Con. 3: Mark Twain. Con. 4:
John Greenleaf Whittier ("Maud Muller").

5-POINT QUESTIONS: Con. 1: J. P. Morgan (in the worst days
of the depression). Con. 2: Thomas Gray ("Elegy in a Country
Churchyard"). Con. 3: Voltaire. Con. 4: Oscar Wilde ("The Picture of Dorian Gray").

FAMOUS SAYINGS—Part 2

2-POINT QUESTIONS: Con. 1: Attributed to Marie Antoinette.
Con. 2: Patrick Henry. Con. 3: Julius Caesar. Con. 4: Winston
Churchill.

3-POINT QUESTIONS: Con. 1: Henry Clay. Con. 2: George
Washington. Con. 3: Oscar Wilde. Con. 4: Davy Crockett.

5-POINT QUESTIONS: Con. 1: Mark Twain. Con. 2: George M.
Cohan. Con. 3: Col. William Prescott at Bunker Hill. Con. 4: John
Donne.

FAMOUS SAYINGS—Part 3

2-POINT QUESTIONS: Con. 1: Abraham Lincoln (June 16, 1858
speech). Con. 2: Calvin Coolidge. Con. 3: Noel Coward (song).
Con. 4: Rudyard Kipling ("Ballad of East and West").

3-POINT QUESTIONS: Admiral Dewey at Manila Bay. Con. 2:

Admiral Farragut at Mobile Bay. Con. 3: Phineas T. Barnum. Con. 4: Ethel Barrymore (Curtain line of "Sunday").

5-POINT QUESTIONS: Con. 1: Madame de Pompadour. Con. 2: Heywood Broun. Con. 3: Nicholas Murray Butler. Con. 4: Charles Dickens (in "David Copperfield").

COMPLETE THE SAYINGS—Part 1

2-POINT QUESTIONS: Con. 1: "is pigs!" (Ellis Parker Butler) Con. 2: "help themselves." (Benjamin Franklin) Con. 3: "who enter here." (Dante) Con. 4: "in the eating." (Cervantes)

3-POINT QUESTIONS: "mankind upon a cross of gold." (William Jennings Bryan) Con. 2: "owed by so many to so few." (Churchill) Con. 3: "Gang aft a-gley." (Robert Burns) Con. 4: "a good thing?" (Cervantes)

5-POINT QUESTIONS: Con. 1: "miles of pedigree" (Dana Burnet) Con. 2: "leads on to fortune." (Shakespeare—Julius Caesar") Con. 3: "knows the price of everything and the value of nothing." (Oscar Wilde) Con. 4: "Heaven will protect the Working Girl!" (Edgar Smith)

COMPLETE THE SAYINGS—Part 2

2-POINT QUESTIONS: Con. 1: "that is news." (John Bogart) Con. 2: "on the beach." (Harry Braisted—song) Con. 3: "to listen." (Ambrose Bierce) Con. 4: "talk of many things." (Lewis Carroll)

3-POINT QUESTIONS: "right with the world." (Robert Browning) Con. 2: "rose is a rose." (Gertrude Stein) Con. 3: "try men's souls." (Thomas Paine) Con. 4: "gets the grease." (Josh Billings)

5-POINT QUESTIONS: Con. 1: "they are painted." (Sir Max Beerbohm) Con. 2: "shade of the trees." (Dying words of Stonewall Jackson) Con. 3: "as optimism." (Arnold Bennett) Con. 4: "falling into her hands." (Ambrose Bierce)

MYTHOLOGY—Part 1

2-POINT QUESTIONS: Con. 1: Atlas. Con. 2: Aurora Borealis. Con. 3: Centaurs. Con. 4: Love (also beauty and fruitfulness).

3-POINT QUESTIONS: Con. 1: He overcame her greater speed by tossing three golden apples in her path as she ran. She stopped to pick them up. Con. 2: The Augean Stables. Con. 3: Three-headed Cerberus. Con. 4: Circe.

5-POINT QUESTIONS: The winged horse, Pegasus. Con. 2: Caduceus, a winged staff entwined by two serpents. Con. 3: Charon. Con. 4: The father was Daedalus, the son Icarus. Icarus' wings melted when he flew too near the sun.

MYTHOLOGY—Part 2

2-POINT QUESTIONS: Con. 1: Cupid. Con. 2: The Golden Fleece. Con. 3: Hercules. Con. 4: Olympus, a mountain in Macedonia.

3-POINT QUESTIONS: Con. 1: Cyclopes (plural for Cyclops). Con. 2: Alexander the Great. Con. 3: Narcissus. Con. 4: Janus, the god of doorways and entrances (January was named after him).

5-POINT QUESTIONS: Con. 1: Because Pluto, who had stolen and married her, had tricked her into eating a pomegranate there, thus making Hades her home. Con. 2: Hector was the great Trojan hero. When he killed Achilles' friend Patroclus, Achilles slew Hector and dragged his body around the walls of Troy. Con. 3: Proteus, from whose name we got the word "protean." Con. 4: The Minotaur, a half-man, half-bull monster.

MYTHOLOGY—Part 3

2-POINT QUESTIONS: Con. 1: Achilles. Con. 2: Helen of Troy. Con. 3: Bacchus. Con. 4: River Styx.

3-POINT QUESTIONS: Con. 1: He was shot in the heel with a poisoned arrow by Paris. Con. 2: The Argonauts. Con. 3: Siegfried. Con. 4: Thor (Thursday was named after him).

5-POINT QUESTIONS: Con. 1: Theseus. Con. 2: (a) Menelaus. (b) Paris of Troy. Con. 3: Perseus was able to behead Medusa by looking at her in the reflection of his bright shield. Con. 4: Tantalus (hence, our word "tantalize").

THE BIBLE—Part 1

2-POINT QUESTIONS: Con. 1: Goliath. Con. 2: John the Baptist. Con. 3: Jerusalem. Con. 4: Jonah.

3-POINT QUESTIONS: Con. 1: Sea of Galilee. Con. 2: Abraham (or Abram). Con. 3: Saul of Tarsus. Con. 4: At Jericho, the defending walls tumbled when the trumpets blew.

5-POINT QUESTIONS: Con 1: Seth, Shem and Japheth. Con. 2: Jacob first married the older daughter, Leah, and later married Rachel. Con. 3: Procurator of Judea. Con. 4: 969 years.

THE BIBLE—Part 2

2-POINT QUESTIONS: Con. 1: Samson. Con. 2: Solomon. Con. 3: Thomas. Con. 4: Sodom and Gomorrah.

3-POINT QUESTIONS: Con. 1: Stephen. Con. 2: Miriam. Con. 3: Joseph. Con. 4: Elijah.

5-POINT QUESTIONS: Con. 1: Caiaphas, the High Priest; Pontius Pilate, the Roman Procurator of Judea; and Herod Antipas, Tetrarch of Galilee. Con. 2: Saul, David and Solomon. Con. 3: Instead of going to Nineveh, Jonah sailed for Tarshish. Con. 4: Joseph of Arimathaea.

THE BIBLE—Part 3

2-POINT QUESTIONS: Con. 1: Tower of Babel. Con. 2: David. Con. 3: Delilah. Con. 4: Nazareth.

3-POINT QUESTIONS: Con. 1: Absalom. Con. 2: Armageddon. Con. 3: Bath-sheba (wife of Uriah). Con. 4: Exodus.

5-POINT QUESTIONS: Con. 1: Ananias. Con. 2: Belshazzar. Con. 3: Cyrus (the Great). Con. 4: Seven.

LEGENDS, TALES AND FABLES—Part 1

2-POINT QUESTIONS: Con. 1: William Tell. Con. 2: Simon Legree. Con. 3: The Flying Dutchman. Con. 4: Fountain of Youth.

3-POINT QUESTIONS: Con. 1: A beautiful lady behind one door,

a fierce tiger behind the other. Con. 2: "Last of the Mohicans."
Con. 3: Midas. Con. 4: The Mormons.

5-POINT QUESTIONS: Con. 1: John Henry. Con. 2: Oliver
Cromwell. Con. 3: Sancho Panza. Con. 4: Thomas à Becket.

LEGENDS, TALES AND FABLES—Part 2

2-POINT QUESTIONS: Con. 1: Friar Tuck. Con. 2: Lady Godiva.
Con. 3: Sinbad the Sailor. Con. 4: Huckleberry Finn.

3-POINT QUESTIONS: Con. 1: Athos, Porthos, and Aramis. Con.
2: The Jabberwock. Con. 3: The phoenix. Con. 4: Jim Hawkins.

5-POINT QUESTIONS: Con. 1: Jack and Jill. Con. 2: Pygmalion.
Con. 3: Napoleon. Con. 4: Modred.

LEGENDS, TALES AND FABLES—Part 3

2-POINT QUESTIONS: Con. 1: Atlantis. Con. 2: The Blarney
Stone. Con. 3: Ali Baba. Con. 4: Lorelei.

3-POINT QUESTIONS: Con. 1: Androcles. Con. 2: Excalibur.
Con. 3: Bruce (or Robert the Bruce). Con. 4: Damon and Pythias.

5-POINT QUESTIONS: Con. 1: Anacreon (the original English
song was "To Anacreon in Heaven"). Con. 2: Bucephalus (meaning ox-headed). Con. 3: Grendel. Con. 4: John and Michael
Darling.

NURSERY RHYMES—Part 1

2-POINT QUESTIONS: Con. 1: Tea. Con. 2: Nine days old. Con.
3: A plum. Con. 4: Under the haystack (fast asleep).

3-POINT QUESTIONS: Con. 1: His master, his dame and the
little boy who lived down the lane. Con. 2: Some broth, without
any bread. Con. 3: Tuesday's child is full of grace. Con. 4: A whale.

5-POINT QUESTIONS: Con. 1: "Over the Hills And Far Away."
Con. 2: Silver buckles. Con. 3: "Are the children in bed? for it's
now eight o'clock." Con. 4: A very fine gander.

NURSERY RHYMES—Part 2

2-POINT QUESTIONS: Con. 1: A spider. Con. 2: The candlestick. Con. 3: A pig. Con. 4: He kissed them.

3-POINT QUESTIONS: Con. 1: Butcher, baker, and candlestick maker. Con. 2: Pie ("Then you shall have no pie!") Con. 3: A wooden shoe. Con. 4: To see a fine lady, upon a white horse.

5-POINT QUESTIONS: Con. 1: They took some honey, and plenty of money, wrapped up in a five-pound note. Con. 2: Dasher, Dancer, Prancer, Vixen, Comet, Cupid, Donner and Blitzen. Con. 3: "Is bonny and bright and good and gay." Con. 4: Ann (who had crept under the pudding pan).

ORIGIN OF WORDS

2-POINT QUESTIONS: Con. 1: Titanic. Con. 2: Hieroglyphics. Con. 3: Scintillate. Con. 4: Bacteria.

3-POINT QUESTIONS: Con. 1: Lethargy. Con. 2: Stentorian. Con. 3: Laconic. Con. 4: Chauvinism.

5-POINT QUESTIONS: Con. 1: Assassins. Con. 2: Admiral. Con. 3: Nepotism. Con. 4: Ostracize.

INTERESTING PLACES—Part 1

2-POINT QUESTIONS: Con. 1: Africa. Con. 2: Australia. Con. 3: Europe. Con. 4: The Alps.

3-POINT QUESTIONS: Con. 1: North. Con. 2: The Himalayas. Con. 3: An ocean area (no land). Con. 4: Caribbean.

5-POINT QUESTIONS: Con. 1: The Bund. Con. 2: U.S. 66. Con. 3: The Appian Way. Con. 4: Easter Island.

INTERESTING PLACES—Part 2

2-POINT QUESTIONS: Con. 1: Arctic Ocean. Con. 2: Elba. Con. 3: English Channel. Con. 4: Dead Sea.

3-POINT QUESTIONS: Con. 1: Danube River. Con. 2: Cairo, Egypt. Con. 3: Austria and Italy. Con. 4: Andes Mountains.

5-POINT QUESTIONS: Con. 1: Florence. Con. 2: Peiping. Con. 3: Fleet Street. Con. 4: Sugar Loaf (Pao de Acucar).

INTERESTING PLACES—Part 3

2-POINT QUESTIONS: Fjord or fiord. Con. 2: Ganges. Con. 3: Iceland. Con. 4: The Po (418 miles).

3-POINT QUESTIONS: Con. 1: Straits of Magellan. Con. 2: Pampas. Con. 3: Chile (over 2600 miles long; often less than 200 miles wide). Con. 4: Genoa.

5-POINT QUESTIONS: Con. 1: Pitcairn Island. Con. 2: Stone Mountain Memorial. Con. 3: Threadneedle Street (the Bank is often called "the Old Lady of Threadneedle Street"). Con. 4: Zambesi River.

INTERESTING PLACES—Part 4

2-POINT QUESTIONS: Con. 1: Alaska. Con. 2: The Amazon. Con. 3: St. Helena. Con. 4: Sahara.

3-POINT QUESTIONS: Con. 1: Bangkok. Con. 2: Pall Mall. Con. 3: Shetland Islands. Con. 4: Kansas.

5-POINT QUESTIONS: Con. 1: Bay of Fundy (over 50 feet). Con. 2: Superior, Michigan, Huron, Erie and Ontario. Con. 3: Sargasso Sea (named from the bladder-like thallus which keeps the seaweed afloat). Con. 4: Hyde Park (Rotten Row is now used by riders).

WHERE ARE YOU? (Name the State)—Part 1

2-POINT QUESTIONS: Con. 1: Wisconsin. Con. 2: Virginia. Con. 3: Texas. Con. 4: Rhode Island.

3-POINT QUESTIONS: Con. 1: Wyoming. Con. 2: Oklahoma. Con. 3: Montana. Con. 4: South Carolina.

5-POINT QUESTIONS: Con. 1: Washington. Con. 2: Utah. Con. 3: Texas. Con. 4: Minnesota.

WHERE ARE YOU? (Name the State)—Part 2

2-POINT QUESTIONS: Con. 1: Tennessee. Con. 2: Massachusetts. Con. 3: Louisiana. Con. 4: Michigan.

3-POINT QUESTIONS: Con. 1: Maine. Con. 2: Minnesota. Con. 3: Missouri. Con. 4: North Carolina.

5-POINT QUESTIONS: Con. 1: Kansas. Con. 2: Nebraska. Con. 3: New York. Con. 4: Pennsylvania.

WHERE ARE YOU? (Name the State)—Part 3

2-POINT QUESTIONS: Con. 1: Alabama. Con. 2: Arizona. Con. 3: Arkansas. Con. 4: California.

3-POINT QUESTIONS: Con. 1: California. Con. 2: Florida. Con. 3: Illinois. Con. 4: Kentucky.

5-POINT QUESTIONS: Con. 1: Colorado. Con. 2: Georgia. Con. 3: Idaho. Con. 4: Indiana.

WHERE ARE THESE RIVERS?—Part 1

2-POINT QUESTIONS: Con. 1: China. Con. 2: Alaska. Con. 3: Austria-Hungary (boundary); also Germany (where it rises). Con. 4: United States-Mexico (boundary).

3-POINT QUESTIONS: Con. 1: India. Con. 2: U.S.S.R. Con. 3: Canada. Con. 4: Germany.

5-POINT QUESTIONS: Con. 1: Indo-China. Con. 2: U.S.S.R. Con. 3: Australia. Con. 4: Brazil.

WHERE ARE THESE RIVERS?—Part 2

2-POINT QUESTIONS: Con. 1: Egypt. Con. 2: Brazil. Con. 3: United States-Canada (boundary). Con. 4: U.S.S.R.

3-POINT QUESTIONS: Con. 1: India. Con. 2: Turkey (and Iraq). Con. 3: Canada. Con. 4: U.S.S.R.

5-POINT QUESTIONS: Con. 1: U.S.S.R. Con. 2: Colombia. Con. 3: Turkey (and Iraq). Con. 4: U.S.S.R.

WHERE ARE THESE FAMOUS STRUCTURES?

2-POINT QUESTIONS: Con. 1: Greece (Athens). Con. 2: Egypt (Giza). Con. 3: Italy (Rome). Con. 4: England (London).

3-POINT QUESTIONS: Con. 1: India (Agra). Con. 2: Italy (Rome); also France (Paris). Con. 3: Spain (Granada). Con. 4: Italy (Venice).

5-POINT QUESTIONS: Con. 1: Turkey (Istanbul). Con. 2: Italy (a cathedral in Florence). Con. 3: Spain (Madrid). Con. 4: Palestine (Jerusalem).

WHERE ARE THESE VOLCANOES?

2-POINT QUESTIONS: Con. 1: Italy. Con. 2: Japan. Con. 3: Hawaii. Con. 4: Mexico.

3-POINT QUESTIONS: Con. 1: United States. Con. 2: Mexico. Con. 3: Sicily. Con. 4: Africa.

5-POINT QUESTIONS: Con. 1: Japan. Con. 2: Sumatra. Con. 3: Alaska. Con. 4: Mexico.

STATE NICKNAMES—Part 1

2-POINT QUESTIONS: Con. 1: Florida. Con. 2: Missouri. Con. 3: Georgia. Con. 4: Kentucky.

3-POINT QUESTIONS: Con. 1: Nebraska. Con. 2: Alabama. Con. 3: Maine. Con. 4: Vermont.

5-POINT QUESTIONS: Con. 1: North Dakota. Con. 2: Arizona. Con. 3: Oregon. Con. 4: Arkansas.

STATE NICKNAMES—Part 2

2-POINT QUESTIONS: Con. 1: Indiana. Con. 2: Louisiana. Con. 3: Pennsylvania. Con. 4: Texas.

3-POINT QUESTIONS: Con. 1: Wisconsin. Con. 2: Connecticut. Con. 3: Kansas. Con. 4: Michigan.

5-POINT QUESTIONS: Con. 1: Iowa. Con. 2: Minnesota. Con. 3: New Hampshire. Con. 4: Oklahoma.

INTERNATIONAL CURRENCY

2-POINT QUESTIONS: Con. 1: India. Con. 2: Italy and Turkey. Con. 3: Holland. Con. 4: Russia.

3-POINT QUESTIONS: Con. 1: China. Con. 2: Greece. Con. 3: Poland. Con. 4: Spain.

5-POINT QUESTIONS: Con. 1: Hungary. Con. 2: Portugal. Con. 3: Yugoslavia, Iran and Iraq. Con. 4: Finland.

AMERICAN HISTORY (Colonial)

2-POINT QUESTIONS: Con. 1: Hudson River, Hudson's Bay.

Con. 2: Isabella and Ferdinand. Con. 3: Nina, Pinta, Santa Maria. Con. 4: Florida.

3-POINT QUESTIONS: Con. 1: Leif Ericson. Con. 2: Amerigo Vespucci. America was named after him. Con. 3: Montezuma. Con. 4: The Pilgrims.

5-POINT QUESTIONS: Con. 1: Powhattan. Con. 2: Virginia Dare (at Roanoke, Va., 1587). Con. 3: Four (1492, 1493, 1498, 1502). Con. 4: Roger Williams—Providence, R. I.

REVOLUTIONARY WAR—Part 1

2-POINT QUESTIONS: Con. 1: "Bon Homme Richard." Con. 2: Valley Forge. Con. 3: Hessians. Con. 4: Minute Men.

3-POINT QUESTIONS: Con. 1: Thomas Paine. Con. 2: Saratoga. Con. 3: The Articles of Confederation. Con. 4: Treaty of Paris.

5-POINT QUESTIONS: Con. 1: Georgia. Con. 2: During the siege of Fort Schuyler in the Mohawk Valley. Con. 3: Spain and Holland. Con. 4: Lt. Col. George Rogers Clark.

REVOLUTIONARY WAR—Part 2

2-POINT QUESTIONS: Con. 1: Liberty or death. Con. 2: Lexington (or Lexington and Concord). Con. 3: Fort Ticonderoga. Con. 4: France.

3-POINT QUESTIONS: Con. 1: The Stamp Act. Con. 2: The Boston Massacre. Con. 3: The Boston Tea Party, where the cargo of three British tea ships was dumped into the harbor to avoid payment of duty on it. Con. 4: First Continental Congress.

5-POINT QUESTIONS: Con. 1: Breed's Hill. Con. 2: Whitehaven. Con. 3: (a) General Henry Clinton, (b) Major John Andre. Con. 4: Samuel Adams and John Hancock.

CIVIL WAR—Part 1

2-POINT QUESTIONS: Con. 1: Fort Sumter. Con. 2: Richmond. Con. 3: West Virginia. Con. 4: General William T. Sherman.

3-POINT QUESTIONS: Con. 1: Hampton Roads (Norfolk, Va.). Con. 2: Missouri. Con. 3: People in the North who quite openly favored the Confederate cause and even shipped to the South information and supplies. Con. 4: Flag Officer, David Farragut.

5-POINT QUESTIONS: Con. 1: The "Virginia." Con. 2: Edward Everett, a noted orator of the day. Con. 3: Gen. Jubal A. Early. Con. 4: Gen. George McClellan.

CIVIL WAR—Part 2

2-POINT QUESTIONS: Con. 1: The Emancipation Proclamation. Con. 2: Stonewall Jackson. Con. 3: Ulysses S. Grant. Con. 4: Appomattox Courthouse.

3-POINT QUESTIONS: Con. 1: Gettysburg and Vicksburg. Con. 2: Gen. Lew Wallace. Con. 3: 1st and 2nd Battles of Bull Run. Con. 4: Edward M. Stanton.

5-POINT QUESTIONS: Con. 1: Gen. George H. Thomas, whose command repulsed Longstreet's fierce attack at bayonet point there. Con. 2: Napoleon III. Con. 3: Maximilian (Ferdinand Maximilian Joseph of Austria). Con. 4: The "Trent Affair."

FIRST WORLD WAR

2-POINT QUESTIONS: Con. 1: The "Lusitania." Con. 2: General John J. Pershing. Con. 3: Ferdinand Foch. Con. 4: Big Bertha.

3-POINT QUESTIONS: Con. 1: Admiral William S. Simms. Con. 2: General Erich von Ludendorff. Con. 3: Belleau Wood (June 6 to July 1, 1918). Con. 4: Franz Ferdinand.

5-POINT QUESTIONS: Con. 1: Battle of Jutland, between the British and German navies. Con. 2: (a) Liberty Loans, (b) Victory Loan. Con. 3: St. Mihiel Salient. Con. 4: Allied Powers: United States, England, France, Italy, Japan, Serbia, Russia, Belgium, Montenegro, Portugal, Rumania and Greece. Central Powers: Germany, Austria-Hungary, Bulgaria and Turkey.

SECOND WORLD WAR—Part 1

2-POINT QUESTIONS: Con. 1: Poland. Con. 2: Erwin Rommel. Con. 3: Douglas MacArthur. Con. 4: They were destroyed at Pearl Harbor.

3-POINT QUESTIONS: Con. 1: The U.S.S. "Panay." Con. 2: 50,000. Con. 3: Albert Einstein. Con. 4: Gen. Charles de Gaulle.

5-POINT QUESTIONS: Con. 1: Freedom of Speech and Expression; Freedom of Worship; Freedom from Want; Freedom from Fear. Con. 2: Greenland. Con. 3: The U.S.S. "Reuben James." Con. 4: Guam, Midway, Philippines, Hong Kong, Malay Peninsula.

SECOND WORLD WAR—Part 2

2-POINT QUESTIONS: Con. 1: Major James Doolittle. Con. 2: Ethiopia. Con. 3: Germany and Russia. Con. 4: Dunkirk.

3-POINT QUESTIONS: Con. 1: The emergency road between Edmonton, Canada, and Fairbanks, Alaska, completed by U. S. Army engineers to help defend Alaska. Con. 2: The National Socialist Party. Con. 3: Denmark and Norway. Con. 4: Sir Winston Churchill, about the R.A.F. in their defense of England against the Luftwaffe.

5-POINT QUESTIONS: Con. 1: The Sudetenland (part of Czechoslovakia). Con. 2: Churchill and Roosevelt: The Atlantic Charter. Con. 3: Joseph C. Grew. Con. 4: El Alamein.

SECOND WORLD WAR—Part 3

2-POINT QUESTIONS: Con. 1: Corregidor. Con. 2: Hiroshima or Nagasaki. Con. 3: The V-1 and V-2 weapons. Con. 4: Normandy.

3-POINT QUESTIONS: Con. 1: Lt. Gen. Walter Short and Rear Adm. Husband Kimmel. Con. 2: Battleship "Prince of Wales," Cruiser "Repulse." Con. 3: Attu, Kiska. Con. 4: Adm. Jean Francois Darlan.

5-POINT QUESTIONS: Con. 1: Battle of Midway (June 3-6, 1942). Con. 2: Battle of Leyte Gulf (Oct. 23-25, 1944). Con. 3: Regensburg, Schweinfurt. Con. 4: Stalingrad.

KOREAN WAR

2-POINT QUESTIONS: Con. 1: The Yalta Conference. Con. 2: 38th parallel. Con. 3: Syngman Rhee. Con. 4: Gen. Douglas MacArthur.

3-point questions: Con. 1: The Pusan Perimeter. Con. 2: Inchon. Con. 3: Yalu River Valley. Con. 4: Panmunjon.

5-point questions: Con. 1: Wake Island. Con. 2: Gen. Matthew B. Ridgway. Con. 3: Chou En-lai. Con. 4: Pyongyang.

U. S. PRESIDENTS—Part 1

2-point questions: Con. 1. Theodore Roosevelt (age 43). Con. 2: James Monroe (in the Monroe Doctrine). Con. 3: George Washington. Con. 4: Harry Truman's (1951).

3-point questions: Con. 1: Thomas Jefferson. Con. 2: John Adams and Thomas Jefferson. Con. 3: George Washington's. Con. 4: Andrew Jackson (who hardly ever consulted his official cabinet but talked affairs of state over with personal friends in his own kitchen).

5-point questions: Con. 1: George Washington and James Madison. Con. 2: Whig. Con. 3: James Buchanan (his fiancée died shortly before their marriage date). Con. 4: James Knox Polk, who finally (1846) settled the Oregon border at the 49th parallel.

U. S. PRESIDENTS—Part 2

2-point questions: Con. 1: William Howard Taft. Con. 2: Abraham Lincoln (6 feet 4). Con. 3. Theodore Roosevelt. Con. 4: Woodrow Wilson.

3-point questions: Con. 1: Thomas Jefferson. Con. 2: Andrew Jackson. Con. 3: William Henry Harrison (died after one month in office). Con. 4: Franklin D. Roosevelt in 1936.

5-point questions: Con. 1: Warren Harding. Con. 2: William McKinley. Con. 3: James Knox Polk. Con. 4: Rutherford B. Hayes.

MILITARY AND NAVAL NAMES

2-point questions: Con. 1: A wooded region in eastern France, scene of a victorious American-French offensive from Sept. 26 to Nov. 6, 1918. Con. 2: Attempts (between 1095 and 1291 A.D.) by the Christian nations of Europe to capture the Holy Land from the Turks. Con. 3: A city in northern Africa which became the political and military rival of Rome. Con. 4: The place of Napoleon's last battle against the Allied Powers of Europe, near Brussels, Belgium, June 18, 1815.

3-POINT QUESTIONS: Con. 1: A Confederate military prison in southwest Georgia. Con. 2: Name given the British troops who suppressed the revolt in Ireland, 1919-1921. Con. 3: The wild butchery of French nobles under the dictatorship of the Committee of Public Safety committed during 1793. Con. 4: An attempt by a strongly nationalistic society of Chinese, called the Boxer Society, to expel all foreigners from China, in 1900.

5-POINT QUESTIONS: Con. 1: Treaty with Germany whereby Russia got out of World War I (March 3, 1918). Con. 2: Important battle in the Boer War (1899). Con. 3: The island near which a Greek fleet in September of 480 B.C. smashed an invading fleet of Persians. Con. 4: The place where Hannibal inflicted a terrible defeat on the Romans, 216 B.C.

THE WILD WEST

2-POINT QUESTIONS: Con. 1: (a) Chief Yellow Hand; (b) Jesse James. Con. 2: The Cisco Kid, created by O. Henry in his short story, "A Caballero's Way." Con. 3: Placer mining. Con. 4: Sutter's Mill.

3-POINT QUESTIONS: Con. 1: 1904 at Goldfield (now a deserted ruin). Con. 2: Barbed wire. Con. 3: Bat Masterson. (Wild Bill Hickok was gunned down by Jack McCall). Con. 4: Completion of the first transcontinental railroad.

5-POINT QUESTIONS: Con. 1: Central Pacific and Union Pacific. Con. 2: John Wesley Hardin, who killed at least 44 men. Con. 3: The Ghost Dance Uprising by the Sioux. Con. 4: The Clanton-McLowery Gang.

NAMES IN SPORTS

2-POINT QUESTIONS: Con. 1: Football. Con. 2: Boxing. Con. 3: Track and Field. Con. 4: Baseball.

3-POINT QUESTIONS: Con. 1: Swimming. Con. 2: Tennis. Con. 3: Boxing. Con. 4: Golf.

5-POINT QUESTIONS: Con. 1: Ice Hockey. Con. 2: Track and Field. Con. 3: Billiards. Con. 4: Basketball (Pro).

FAMOUS EVENTS IN BASEBALL

2-POINT QUESTIONS: Con. 1: Fred Merkle. Con. 2: Christy Mathewson (1905). Con. 3: Rube Marquard (1913). Con. 4: Don Larsen (1956).

3-POINT QUESTIONS: Con. 1: Boston vs. Brooklyn. Con. 2: Johnny Vander Meer. Con. 3: Pete Alexander. Con. 4: Lou Gehrig.

5-POINT QUESTIONS: Con. 1: Joe Jackson, Ty Cobb, Rogers Hornsby, George Sisler, Bill Terry, Harry Heilman, and Ted Williams. Con. 2: 56. Con. 3: 26. Con. 4: Lefty Gomez: won 6, lost 0.

BASEBALL NICKNAMES

2-POINT QUESTIONS: Con. 1: Ty Cobb. Con. 2: Phil Rizzuto. Con. 3: Frank Frisch. Con. 4: Paul Waner.

3-POINT QUESTIONS: Con. 1: Walter Johnson. Con. 2: Elwood Roe. Con. 3: Lynwood Rowe. Con. 4: Bill Terry.

5-POINT QUESTIONS: Con. 1: Harry Brecheen. Con. 2: Honus Wagner. Con. 3: Pete Reiser. Con. 4: Mickey Cochrane.

WHO SAID IT?

2-POINT QUESTIONS: Con. 1: Willie Mays. Con. 2: Leo Durocher. Con. 3: Bill Terry. Con. 4: Dizzy Dean (about himself and his brother, Paul, in the World Series).

3-POINT QUESTIONS: Con. 1: Willie Keeler, on how to hit .350. Con. 2: John L. Sullivan, on losing the heavyweight title to Jim Corbett. Con. 3: Joe Louis, about Billy Conn. Con. 4: Chuck Dressen, in August 1951 (when the Giants beat his Dodgers for the National League title).

5-POINT QUESTIONS: Con. 1: A Chicago boy to Shoeless Joe Jackson, about the "Black Sox" scandal. Con. 2: Joe Jacobs, over Max Schmeling's loss to Jack Sharkey. Con. 3: Bob Fitzsimmons, about his forthcoming bout with Jim Jeffries. Con. 4: Leroy (Satchel) Paige, in his advice on longevity in sports.

POPULAR MUSIC—Part 1

2-POINT QUESTIONS: Con. 1: A dame! Con. 2: A gun. Con. 3: Glocca Morra. Con. 4: "We're in love."

3-POINT QUESTIONS: Con. 1: Atchison, Topeka and Santa Fe. Con. 2: "Kiss Me Much." Con. 3: Charleston. Con. 4: South America.

5-POINT QUESTIONS: Con. 1: *Second Piano Concerto.* Con. 2: "Liliom." Con. 3: *The Polonaise.* Con. 4: *Fantasie Impromptu.*

POPULAR MUSIC—Part 2

2-POINT QUESTIONS: Con. 1: Music. Con. 2: Show business. Con. 3: "Over There." Con. 4: "When You Wish Upon A Star."

3-POINT QUESTIONS: Con. 1: Buttermilk. Con. 2: Lena Horne. Con. 3: Nick Kenny. Con. 4: "The Singing Fool."

5-POINT QUESTIONS: Con. 1: "Lili Marlene." Con. 2: Cole Porter. Con. 3: Claude Debussy. Con. 4: William Christopher (W. C.) Handy.

CLASSICAL MUSIC

2-POINT QUESTIONS: Con. 1: Richard Wagner. Con. 2: Giuseppe Verdi. Con. 3: Edvard Grieg. Con. 4: Stephen Foster.

3-POINT QUESTIONS: Con. 1: Maurice Ravel. Con. 2: Ludwig von Beethoven. Con. 3: Frederic Chopin. Con. 4: Sergei Rachmaninoff.

5-POINT QUESTIONS: Con. 1: Camille Saint-Saens. Con. 2: Opera. Con. 3: George Frederick Handel. Con. 4: Franz Joseph Haydn.

OPERAS

2-POINT QUESTIONS: Con. 1: "Madame Butterfly." Con. 2: "Faust." Con. 3: "Hansel and Gretel." Con. 4: "Carmen."

3-POINT QUESTIONS: Con. 1: "La Boheme." Con. 2: "The Girl of the Golden West." Con. 3: "Tannhauser." Con. 4: "Mignon."

5-POINT QUESTIONS: Con. 1: "Lakme." Con. 2: "Lucia di Lammermoor." Con. 3: "Rigoletto." Con. 4: "Thais."

THEME SONGS

2-POINT QUESTIONS: Con. 1: Mary Martin. Con. 2: Jack Benny. Con. 3: Ezio Pinza. Con. 4: George M. Cohan.

3-POINT QUESTIONS: Con. 1: Elvis Presley. Con. 2: Al Jolson. Con. 3: Frankie Laine. Con. 4: Bob Hope.

5-POINT QUESTIONS: Con. 1: Paul Whiteman. Con. 2: Juanita Hall, as "Bloody Mary." Con. 3: The Andrews Sisters. Con. 4: Nora Bayes.

SHOW BUSINESS

2-POINT QUESTIONS: Con. 1: Olsen and Johnson. Con. 2: The Palace. Con. 3: Yul Brynner. Con. 4: Will Rogers.

3-POINT QUESTIONS: Con. 1: Jascha Heifetz, Yehudi Menuhin, Fritz Kreisler. Con. 2: "Jumbo." Con. 3: Fred Allen. Con. 4: "Life With Father" (3224), "Tobacco Road" (3182), "Abie's Irish Rose" (2327).

5-POINT QUESTIONS: Con. 1: Helen Hayes: "Victoria Regina." Con. 2: Walter Winchell. Con. 3: Vincent Lopez. Con. 4: "Our American Cousin."

ART

2-POINT QUESTIONS: Con. 1: Alba. Con. 2: Michelangelo. Con. 3: England. Con. 4: The "Mona Lisa."

3-POINT QUESTIONS: Con. 1: St. Francis of Assisi. Con. 2: Raphael. Con. 3: Jacopo Bellini. Con. 4: Titian.

5-POINT QUESTIONS: Con. 1: Andrea de Castagno. Con. 2: Leonardo da Vinci. Con. 3: Jan and Hubert van Eyck. Con. 4: Hans Holbein.

INVENTORS

2-POINT QUESTIONS: Con. 1: Steamboat. Con. 2: Revolver. Con. 3: Telegraph. Con. 4: Sleeping car for railroads.

3-POINT QUESTIONS: Con. 1: The reaper (farming). Con. 2: Carpet sweeper. Con. 3: Passenger elevator. Con. 4: Vulcanization of rubber.

5-POINT QUESTIONS: Con. 1: Iconoscope tube for television. Con. 2: Linotype machine. Con. 3: Sewing machine. Con. 4: Air brake for railroads.

FAMOUS PEOPLE—Part 1

2-POINT QUESTIONS: Con. 1: Socrates. Con. 2: King John. Con. 3: Sir Isaac Newton. Con. 4: Mary Pickford.

3-POINT QUESTIONS: Con. 1: Florence Nightingale. Con. 2: Walt Whitman. Con. 3: Benvenuto Cellini. Con. 4: Jean and Auguste Picard.

5-POINT QUESTIONS: Con. 1: Wilhelm Röentgen. Con. 2: Titian. Con. 3: Friedrich Engels. Con. 4: General Winfield Scott.

FAMOUS PEOPLE—Part 2

2-POINT QUESTIONS: Con. 1: Alexander the Great. Con. 2: Albert Einstein. Con. 3: Henry VIII. Con. 4: Herbert Hoover.

3-POINT QUESTIONS: Con. 1: Sir Francis Drake. Con. 2: Francis of Assisi. Con. 3: William Randolph Hearst. Con. 4: Sam Houston.

5-POINT QUESTIONS: Con. 1: Sun Yat-sen. Con. 2: Baron Fredrick von Steuben. Con. 3: Voltaire. Con. 4: Pythagoras.

FAMOUS PEOPLE—Part 3

2-POINT QUESTIONS: Con. 1: Davy Crockett. Con. 2: Paul Goebbels. Con. 3: King Farouk. Con. 4: Marco Polo.

3-POINT QUESTIONS: Con. 1: Sigmund Freud. Con. 2: Euclid. Con. 3: Horace Greeley. Con. 4: Marie Antoinette.

5-POINT QUESTIONS: Con. 1: George Goethals. Con. 2: Aleksandr Kerenski. Con. 3: Pliny the Elder. Con. 4: Tomas de Torquemada.

FAMOUS PEOPLE—Part 4

2-POINT QUESTIONS: Con. 1: Nathan Hale. Con. 2: Joan of Arc. Con. 3: Haile Selassie. Con. 4: Captain Myles Standish.

3-POINT QUESTIONS: Con. 1: John Sutter. Con. 2: Diogenes. Con. 3: Martin Luther. Con. 4: Sir Thomas Lipton.

5-POINT QUESTIONS: Con. 1: Charlotte Corday. Con. 2: Stephen Decatur. Con. 3: Zoroaster or Zarathustra, founder of Zoroastrianism. Con. 4: Joseph Priestley.

FAMOUS PEOPLE—Part 5

2-POINT QUESTIONS: Con. 1: Calvin Coolidge. Con. 2: Amelia Earhart. Con. 3: Thomas Edison. Con. 4: Josephine (Marie de la Pagerie).

3-POINT QUESTIONS: Con. 1: Hannibal. Con. 2: Clarence Darrow. Con. 3: Demosthenes. Con. 4: Mary Baker Eddy.

5-POINT QUESTIONS: Con. 1: Kemal Ataturk (Mustava Kemal Pascha). Con. 2: William McGuffey. Con. 3: Blaise Pascal. Con. 4: Pompey.

FAMOUS PEOPLE—Part 6

2-POINT QUESTIONS: Con. 1: John Quincy Adams. Con. 2: Enrico Caruso. Con. 3: Jefferson Davis. Con. 4: Pierre and Marie Curie.

3-POINT QUESTIONS: Con. 1: Karl "Baron" Munchausen. Con. 2: Alfred Nobel (founder of the Nobel prizes). Con. 3: Admiral Lord Horatio Nelson. Con. 4: Mohammed.

5-POINT QUESTIONS: Con. 1: Nikolaus Copernicus. Con. 2: Samuel Gompers. Con. 3: Vasco da Gama. Con. 4: Allan Pinkerton.

FAMOUS EXPLORERS

2-POINT QUESTIONS: Con. 1: Pacific Ocean. Con. 2: Florida. Con. 3: Mississippi River. Con. 4: Straits of Magellan, or Philippine Islands, or first expedition around the world (accept any).

3-POINT QUESTIONS: Con. 1: Mexico. Con. 2: Peru. Con. 3: Mississippi River region. Con. 4: Labrador or east coast of Canada.

SCIENCE—Part 1

2-POINT QUESTIONS: Con. 1: Liquid and gas. Con. 2: Gold. Con. 3: Warm air. At 32 degrees Fahrenheit, sound travels at about 1090 feet per second at sea level. Its velocity speeds up about 1 foot per second for each higher degree in air temperature. Con. 4: Bauxite.

3-POINT QUESTIONS: Con. 1: Its specific gravity. Con. 2: Osmosis. Con. 3: Some energy must be expended in overcoming friction. Con. 4: The Law of Conservation of Energy, or the First Law of Thermodynamics.

5-POINT QUESTIONS: Con. 1: That a body at rest remains at rest (possesses inertia), and a body in motion moves with uniform velocity in a straight line (has inertia of motion) unless it is compelled to change its position by an external force. Con. 2: With every action (or force), there is an equal reaction in the opposite direction. Con. 3: In most compounds, carbon has a valence of 4. Con. 4: Hydrogen.

SCIENCE—Part 2

2-POINT QUESTIONS: Con. 1: The sun and the moon. Con. 2: The barometer. Con. 3: 186,000 miles per second. Con. 4: Smallpox.

3-POINT QUESTIONS: Con. 1: The Greeks (of Iona). Con. 2: Hippocrates. Con. 3: Ptolemy. Con. 4: Galileo.

5-POINT QUESTIONS: Con. 1: Aristotle. Con. 2: Lavoisier. Con. 3: Gregor Johann Mendel. Con. 4: Dmitri Mendelejeff.

THE HUMAN BODY

2-POINT QUESTIONS: Con. 1: They are muscles. Con. 2: They are bones. Con. 3: In the ear. Con. 4: Carbon dioxide.

3-POINT QUESTIONS: Con. 1: The digestive (gastro-intestinal) system. Con. 2: The throat (upper respiratory tract). Con. 3: The nervous system (brain). Con. 4: The liver.

5-POINT QUESTIONS: Con. 1: 206. Con. 2: Metabolism is the process by which food and air are converted into energy and body tissue. Con. 3: An acute bacterial infectious disease causing glandular swelling. Rabbits are the main carriers. Con. 4: To carry oxygen from the lungs to the body tissues.

ABBREVIATIONS

2-POINT QUESTIONS: Con. 1: Madame. Con. 2: Esquire. Con. 3: Reverend. Con. 4: Rural Free Delivery.

3-POINT QUESTIONS: Con. 1: Temporary National Economic Commission. Con. 2: Works Projects (or Progress) Administration. Con. 3: Tennessee Valley Authority. Con. 4: Union of Soviet Socialist Republics.

5-POINT QUESTIONS: Con. 1: Supreme Headquarters, Allied Expeditionary Force. Con. 2: Supreme Headquarters, Allied Powers in Europe. Con. 3: United Nations Relief and Rehabilitation Administration. Con. 4: United Nations Educational, Scientific and Cultural Organization.

POT LUCK—Part 1

2-POINT QUESTIONS: Con. 1: The Sioux Indians for whom he led combined Indian forces at the Battle of Little Big Horn. Con. 2: Solon was the Chief Magistrate of Athens who compiled the most equitable legal code the world had known. (He died in 559 B.C.) Con. 3: Miki Kuchi is Mickey Mouse. Con. 4: A rook (from the Persian word "rukh," meaning castle) is one of the pieces used in chess.

3-POINT QUESTIONS: Con. 1: Jezebel. Con. 2: Criticized for the appointment of friends to high political office, Andrew Jackson epitomized the "spoils" system with that saying. Con. 3: Mercury is closest to the sun. Con. 4: The abacus, probably first invented by the Chinese, but independently invented by the Egyptians in 500 B.C.

POT LUCK—Part 2

2-POINT QUESTIONS: Con. 1: Steve Brodie. Con. 2: Mexican War (1846-1848). Con. 3: Governor Peter Minuit. Con. 4: Pandora.

3-POINT QUESTIONS: Con. 1: The author of the Third Gospel and of the Acts of the Apostle was Luke, a physician. Con. 2: It's from the Chinese words "ko" and "tou," which mean to knock the head on the ground, to prostrate one's self. Con. 3: The song "Comin' Thru the Rye" commemorates an old practice whereby a young man, who met a young girl on the stepping stones across the River Rye in Scotland, could exact a kiss. Con. 4: Jane Burke, born at Princeton, Mo., in 1852, was a real government mail carrier between South Dakota and Montana, an Indian scout for General Custer, and an Army scout for General Miles. She was nicknamed "Calamity Jane."

5-POINT QUESTIONS: Con. 1: President James Polk. Con. 2: Queen Elizabeth I, daughter of Henry VIII and Anne Boleyn. Con. 3: The pelican of the South Pacific is called a Cormorant. Con. 4: 62.4 pounds.

POT LUCK—Part 3

2-POINT QUESTIONS: Con. 1: Shakespeare's "Hamlet." Con. 2: Parson Weems created the legend that as a boy George Washington chopped down his father's cherry tree. Con. 3: Andrew Jackson. Con. 4: Statue of Liberty.

3-POINT QUESTIONS: Con. 1: He referred to people in the newspaper field. Con. 2: The bat is a mammal; therefore it is more closely related biologically to the cow than to birds or insects. Con. 3: The Progressive Party. Their candidate was Theodore Roosevelt. Con. 4: A bushmaster is a poisonous snake, a member of the rattlesnake family.

5-POINT QUESTIONS: Con. 1: In Grant's own memoirs there is

this record: "There was no demand made for General Lee's sword, and no tender made of it." Con. 2: St. Augustine, Florida, founded by the Spaniards in 1565. Con. 3: Photosynthesis. Con. 4: Gabriele D'Annunzio (1864-1938).

POT LUCK—Part 4

2-POINT QUESTIONS: Con. 1: The "White House" was so named by Theodore Roosevelt. Con. 2: Atlanta. Con. 3: A German submarine torpedoed it. Con. 4: Hessians. The British hired 20,000 of them from the Duke of Brunswick in the State of Hesse, in southwestern Germany.

3-POINT QUESTIONS: Con. 1: Zero. The German physicist Fahrenheit's mistake (in the 18th century) in setting the freezing point of water at 32 degrees was corrected in the Centigrade thermometer, which sets that point at zero. Con. 2: The legendary founders of Rome were brothers Romulus and Remus. Con. 3: The great city which straddles the Bosphorus and is therefore situated in both Europe and Asia is Istambul, formerly known as Constantinople. Con. 4: Uruguay.

5-POINT QUESTIONS: Caries are tooth cavities; myopia is nearsightedness; missing patellar reflex is missing knee jerk. Con. 2: The horse-seeking king was Richard III. Con. 3: Penicillin was discovered by Sir Alexander Fleming. Con. 4: The Bubonic Plague ("Black Death") occurred in Europe in the 14th Century, reaching its climax in 1348. The Hundred Years War between France and England ran, with truces, from 1337 to 1453! The plague was so severe that it interrupted the war.

POT LUCK—Part 5

2-POINT QUESTIONS: Con. 1: Yukon. Con. 2: Yankee Doodle. Con. 3: Benjamin Franklin, the Founding Father who favored 5:00 A.M. alarm-clock settings. Con. 4: Queen Victoria. Disraeli was Prime Minister of England in 1868-1869 and 1874-1880.

3-POINT QUESTIONS: Con. 1: Venus. Con. 2: "The Thinker." Con. 3: New York University. Con. 4: Major Alfred Dreyfus, the central figure in France's most famous military trial—a man championed by Emile Zola and Georges Clemenceau.

5-POINT QUESTIONS: Con. 1: Edward M. Stanton. Con. 2: Richard Gatling. (He started work on his machine gun in 1861. It was accepted by the U. S. Army in 1866.) Con. 3: The mathematician-strategist of Syracuse was Archimedes (287-212 B.C.), also famous for discovering the law of specific gravity. Con. 4: Napoleon, addressing his soldiers in Egypt, July 21, 1798.

POT LUCK—Part 6

2-POINT QUESTIONS: The Mississippi and the Missouri Rivers are 4,194 miles in length. Con. 2: Boston. Con. 3: Fact. It was destroyed in the year 1091 and later rebuilt. Con. 4: Paris and London.

3-POINT QUESTIONS: Con. 1: Cremona, Italy (1649-1737). Con. 2: In crossing the International Date Line from East to West, you SUBTRACT one day from the calendar. Going the other way, you ADD a day. Con. 3: Scheherazade (The Arabian Nights). Con. 4: Ann Rutledge.

5-POINT QUESTIONS: Con. 1: E Pluribus Unum is a Latin phrase meaning "One out of many." John Adams suggested it as a motto. Con. 2: Graf Spee. Con. 3: The second wife of Julius Caesar was Pompeia, who was related to Caesar's ultimate enemy, Pompey. Con. 4: (1) Calamity Jane; (2) James "Wild Bill" Hickok.

POT LUCK—Part 7

2-POINT QUESTIONS: Con. 1: The explosion of the Zeppelin "Hindenburg." Con. 2: The seaport, Mobile; the song, "On Mobile Bay." Con. 3: The smaller the animal, the higher the pulse rate. The mouse has about 700 beats per minute, the elephant, about 30. Con. 4: It was Job who developed patience out of great affliction.

3-POINT QUESTIONS: Con. 1: Kaiser Wilhelm. Con. 2: San Antonio. Con. 3: Thomas Jefferson. Con. 4: "Even the walls have ears."

5-POINT QUESTIONS: Con. 1: Demosthenes was trying to rouse the Athenians against the territorial encroachments of Philip of

Macedon. Con. 2: William Henry Harrison, our 9th President, contracted pneumonia from reviewing the inauguration parade bareheaded, and died after a month in office. Con. 3: Whales eat plankton. Con. 4: (a) They represented the South; (b) to arrange for an armistice; (c) the meeting failed because Jefferson Davis insisted on independence for the South.

POT LUCK—Part 8

2-POINT QUESTIONS: Con. 1:
"In the Spring a young man's fancy
Lightly turns to thoughts of love."
Con. 2: That brother and sister team were expert poisoners. Con. 3: 239,000 miles. Con. 4: This was the most famous double-play combination of all time (Chicago Cubs).

3-POINT QUESTIONS: Con. 1: The doughboy's conventional means of overland travel in France was a freight-car labelled "Quarante Hommes et Huit Chevaux," meaning 40 men and 8 horses. Con. 2: An "accessory before the fact" is someone who knew that another person intended to commit an offense and—although absent when the offense was committed—did nothing to reveal it to the authorities. Con. 3: Anzio. Con. 4: Ambrosia.

5-POINT QUESTIONS: Con. 1: P-40, War Hawk; P-47, Thunderbolt; P-51, Mustang; B-24, Liberator. Con. 2: Vicksburg, Mississippi; Ticonderoga, New York; Tippecanoe, Indiana; Little Big Horn, Montana. Con. 3: The Battle of Lookout Mountain, at Chattanooga (Nov. 24, 1863), which took place above a heavy mist on the mountain; hence the name. Con. 4: Montreal (because all of its streets are named after saints).

POT LUCK—Part 9

2-POINT QUESTIONS: Con. 1: Rumpelstiltskin. Con. 2: The dodo was a large, clumsy bird, last seen in the Mauritius Islands in the 17th century. Con. 3: China. Con. 4: "U.S.S. Caine."

3-POINT QUESTIONS: Con. 1: Philip II of Macedon. Con. 2: (1) Herbert Hoover. (2) Woodrow Wilson. (3) William Henry Harrison. Con. 3: One meaning is to adhere, to cling; the other is to divide, cut and rive asunder. Con. 4: The Analects are the collected sayings of Confucius and his disciples.

5-POINT QUESTIONS: Con. 1: Electoral winner, Benjamin Harrison, Republican; loser, Grover Cleveland, Democrat. Con. 2: The cormorant (from the Latin corvus marinus, raven of the sea). Con. 3: The stone was found at Fort St. Julien, near Rosetta, in the Nile Delta; hence the name Rosetta Stone. Con. 4: They were the first ships to cross the Atlantic Ocean entirely under steam power (14 days).

POT LUCK—Part 10

2-POINT QUESTIONS: Con. 1: "Peace in our time" was the Return-from-Munich promise of Neville Chamberlain. Con. 2: (2) Grotesque figures on buildings. Con. 3: Physicians take the "Oath of Hippocrates." It is an oath protecting the secrets of the sick room, which Hippocrates, the "Father of Medicine," required the graduates of his school of medicine to take in the 4th Century B.C. Con. 4: Becky Thatcher.

3-POINT QUESTIONS: Con. 1: New Orleans victor was Andrew Jackson. Buena Vista victor was Zachary Taylor. Con. 2: "Babe." Con. 3: New Hampshire (only 13 miles). Con. 4: The Amazon River, after the Amazons.

5-POINT QUESTIONS: Con. 1: Blue, green, red, yellow, orange, and violet (or indigo). Con. 2: Joseph Conrad. Con. 3: "One more such victory and Pyrrhus is undone"—hence, a Pyrrhic victory. Con. 4: Santa Maria delle Grazie in the city, Milan.

POT LUCK—Part 11

2-POINT QUESTIONS: Con. 1: The African bull elephant reaches 11 ft. shoulder height; the Indian elephant, only 9 ft. The African elephant is correspondingly heavier. Con. 2: The center of a whirlpool is called its vortex, from the Latin verb "vertere," meaning "to turn." Con. 3: Napoleon was the Emperor. Con. 4: The earth's surface is 71% covered by water.

3-POINT QUESTIONS: Con. 1: Pluto was the Greek god of the lower world. Con. 2: Andrew Jackson married Rachel Robards.

Legal uncertainties about her previous divorce were never clarified.
Con. 3: Cleopatra and Mark Antony. Con. 4: On May 24, 1844,
those words were sent over the first telegraph line (between Washington and Baltimore) by inventor Samuel Finley Morse.

5-POINT QUESTIONS: Con. 1: The seals' favorite maternity-
hospital site is the Pribilof Islands. Con. 2: The hero of Salamis was
Themistocles (whom the Greeks exiled for life 9 years later). Con.
3: Matthew Brady, Lincoln's favorite lensman. Con. 4: Scotch
patriots stole the Stone of Scone, on which Scottish kings were once
crowned. It has been returned.

POT LUCK—Part 12

2-POINT QUESTIONS: Con. 1: It was Old King Cole who called
for his pipe, his bowl and his fiddlers three. Con. 2: A passage by
sea, from Europe to Asia, through or around the North American
Continent. Columbus, Drake and Henry Hudson tried to find it.
Con. 3: Gary Cooper. Con. 4: Baseball. The squeeze-play is a bunt
executed to score a runner from third base.

3-POINT QUESTIONS: Con. 1: The female cuckoo. Con. 2:
Amsterdam, Holland. Con. 3: The Germans trusted the Siegfried
Line. Con. 4: Harry Greb.

5-POINT QUESTIONS: Con. 1: Julius Caesar. Con. 2: Ogle-
thorpe-Georgia; John Smith-Virginia; Increase Mather-Massachu-
setts. Con. 3: The fact that so many of them hid out in impene-
trable swamps. Con. 4: Kentucky, Missouri, Tennessee, Arkansas
and Mississippi.

POT LUCK—Part 13

2-POINT QUESTIONS: Con. 1: The revenge-seeking Apache
Indian Chief was "Geronimo." Con. 2: Toga. It was the badge of
Roman citizenship. Con. 3: Abraham Lincoln. Con. 4: The Aztec
Indians (or Nehua).

3-POINT QUESTIONS: Con. 1: The Loch Ness Monster. Con. 2:
Halley's Comet, which turns up every 76 years and was first recorded by man in 240 B.C. Con. 3: "Maverick." The ornery Texan

who wouldn't brand his cattle was Samuel Maverick. Con. 4: A member of the Sultan's guard—an organization which dates back to the 14th century.

5-POINT QUESTIONS: Con. 1: Nebuchadnezzar, who built the Hanging Gardens of Babylon. Con. 2: Burnside, Custer, McClellan, Grant, and Kearny were with the North; Jackson, Lee, Buckner, Longstreet, and Hampton were with the South. Con. 3: Captain James Cook. Con. 4: The raven.